Holt
Mathematics

Course 3
Homework and Practice
Workbook

HOLT, RINEHART AND WINSTON

A Harcourt Education Company

Orlando • **Austin** • New York • San Diego • London

CONTENTS

Holt Mathematics

CONTENTS, *CONTINUED*

Holt Mathematics

CONTENTS, *CONTINUED*

Holt Mathematics

CONTENTS, *CONTINUED*

Holt Mathematics

Name _____ Date _____ Class _____

Variables and Expressions

Evaluate each expression for the given value of the variable.

1. $6x + 2$ for $x = 3$

2. $18 - a$ for $a = 13$

_____

_____

3. $\frac{1}{4}y$ for $y = 16$

4. $9 - 2b$ for $b = 3$

_____

_____

5. $44 - 12n$ for $n = 3$

6. $7.2 + 8k$ for $k = 2$

_____

_____

7. $20(b - 15)$ for $b = 19$

8. $n(18 - 5)$ for $n = 4$

_____

_____

Evaluate each expression for the given value of the variables.

9. $2x + y$ for $x = 7$ and $y = 11$

10. $4j - k$ for $j = 4$ and $k = 10$

_____

_____

11. $9a - 6b$ for $a = 6$ and $b = 2$

12. $5s + 5t$ for $s = 15$ and $t = 12$

_____

_____

13. $7(n - m)$ for $m = 4$ and $n = 15$

14. $w(14 - y)$ for $w = 8$ and $y = 5$

_____

_____

If q is the number of quarts of lemonade, then $\frac{1}{4}\,q$ can be used to find the number of cups of lemonade mix needed to make the lemonade. How much mix is needed to make each amount of lemonade?

15. 2 quarts   **16.** 8 quarts   **17.** 12 quarts   **18.** 18 quarts

_____   _____   _____   _____

19. If m is the number of minutes a taxi ride lasts, then $2 + 0.35m$ can be used to find the cost of a taxi ride with Bill's Taxi Company.

How much will it cost for a 12-min taxi ride? _____

1

Holt Mathematics

Name _____ Date _____ Class _____

Write an algebraic expression for each word phrase.

1. 6 less than twice *x*

2. 1 more than the quotient of 21 and *b*

_____

3. 3 times the sum of *b* and 5

4. 10 times the difference of *d* and 3

_____

5. the sum of 11 times *s* and 3

6. 7 minus the product of 2 and *x*

_____

Write a word phrase for each algebraic expression.

7. $2n + 4$

8. $3r - 1$

_____

9. $10 - 6n$

10. $7 + \dfrac{2}{c}$

_____

11. $15x - 12$

12. $\dfrac{y}{5} + 8$

_____

13. Maddie earns $8 per hour. Write an algebraic expression to evaluate how much money Maddie will earn if she works for 15, 20, 25, or 30 hours.

n		Earnings
15		
20		
25		
30		

14. Write a word problem that can be evaluated by the algebraic expression $y - 95$, and evaluate it for $y = 125$.

_____

_____

Holt Mathematics

LESSON 1-3 Practice
Integers and Absolute Value

Write the integers in order from least to greatest.

1. 7, 3, −9

2. −6, 2, −5

3. −4, 1, −1

_____

_____

_____

4. −8, 2, −11

5. −12, −15, 0

6. −24, −17, 30

_____

_____

_____

7. 16, −14, −7

8. −9, −7, −16

9. −19, −23, −10

_____

_____

_____

Find the additive inverse of each integer.

10. −8

11. 6

12. −14

13. 29

_____

_____

_____

_____

Evaluate each expression.

14. $|-8| + |-4|$

15. $|-12| + |12|$

16. $|19| + |-8|$

_____

_____

_____

17. $|29 - 16|$

18. $|35 - 9|$

19. $|14 - 14|$

_____

_____

_____

20. $|-15| + |10|$

21. $|-9| + |30|$

22. $|24| + |-8|$

_____

_____

_____

23. Natalie keeps track of her bowling scores. The scores for the games she played this Saturday relative to her best score last Saturday are Game A, 6; Game B, -3; Game C, 8; and Game D, −5. Use <, >, or = to compare her first two games. Then list her games in order from the lowest score to the highest.

_____

_____

Holt Mathematics

Name _____ Date _____ Class _____

Practice
Adding Integers

Use a number line to find each sum.

1. $3 + 1$

_____

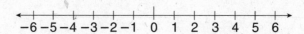

2. $-3 + 2$

_____

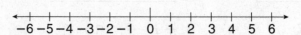

Add.

3. $-5 + 18$ 4. $-10 + 17$ 5. $-22 + (-9)$ 6. $24 + (-15)$

_____   _____   _____   _____

Evaluate each expression for the given value of the variable.

7. $r + 7$ for $r = 3$ 8. $m + 5$ for $m = 9$ 9. $x + 9$ for $x = 4$

_____   _____

10. $-6 + t$ for $t = -8$ 11. $-7 + y$ for $y = -4$ 12. $x + 9$ for $x = -8$

_____   _____   _____

13. $-5 + d$ for $d = -2$ 14. $x + (-4)$ for $x = -4$ 15. $k + (-3)$ for $k = -5$

_____   _____   _____

16. $-8 + b$ for $b = 13$ 17. $-10 + d$ for $d = -2$ 18. $t + (-3)$ for $t = 3$

_____   _____   _____

19. Joleen has 2560 trading cards in her collection. She buys 165 new cards for the collection. How many trading cards does she have now?

_____

20. The running back for the Bears carries the ball twice in the first quarter. The first run he gained fifteen yards and the second run he lost eight yards. How many yards did the two runs total?

_____

Holt Mathematics

Name _____ Date _____ Class _____

Practice
Subtracting Integers

Subtract.

1. 8 − 2

2. 10 − 5

3. 7 − 12

4. 16 − 10

_____

_____

_____

_____

5. 3 − 10

6. 16 − 9

7. −4 − 9

8. −8 − 10

_____

_____

_____

_____

9. 33 − 57

10. 16 − 49

11. −114 − 19

12. −88 − (−10)

_____

_____

_____

_____

Evaluate each expression for the given value of the variable.

13. $x − 8$ for $x = 10$

14. $w − 10$ for $w = 15$

15. $15 − w$ for $w = 8$

_____

_____

_____

16. $12 − t$ for $t = −8$

17. $15 − x$ for $x = −12$

18. $w − 20$ for $w = −15$

_____

_____

_____

19. $−15 − x$ for $x = −10$

20. $−9 − x$ for $x = −20$

21. $−11 − d$ for $d = −15$

_____

_____

_____

22. $y − (−10)$ for $y = −10$

23. $x − (−15)$ for $x = −5$

24. $a − (−12)$ for $a = 10$

_____

_____

_____

25. The altitude of Mt. Blackburn in Alaska is 16,390 feet. The altitude of Mt. Elbert in Colorado is 14,433 feet. What is the difference in the altitudes of the two mountains?

_____

26. In January, Jesse weighed 230 pounds. By November, he weighed 185 pounds. How much did Jesse's weight change?

_____

Holt Mathematics

LESSON 1-6 Practice
Multiplying and Dividing Integers

Multiply or divide.

1. $6 \cdot 7$

2. $\dfrac{-15}{5}$

3. $-7 \cdot 3$

4. $\dfrac{20}{-4}$

_____

5. $\dfrac{-36}{-4}$

6. $-8(-9)$

7. $\dfrac{-48}{-6}$

8. $7(-7)$

_____

9. $5(-8)$

10. $(-6)(-9)$

11. $\dfrac{-36}{4}$

12. $\dfrac{42}{-7}$

_____

13. $-9(-3)$

14. $(-4)(8)$

15. $\dfrac{-54}{-9}$

16. $\dfrac{-72}{8}$

_____

Simplify.

17. $-5(3 + 7)$

18. $10(8 - 2)$

19. $-4(12 - 3)$

20. $9(15 - 8)$

_____

21. $12(-9 + 4)$

22. $-11(7 - 13)$

23. $15(-12 + 8)$

24. $-10(-8 - 6)$

_____

25. $6(-12 + 1)$

26. $-5(3 - 12)$

27. $-8(-5 - 5)$

28. $7(12 - 3)$

_____

29. $10(-7 - 1)$

30. $12(2 - 5)$

31. $-15(-2 - 1)$

32. $9(8 - 20)$

_____

33. Kristin and her three friends buy a pizza with twelve slices and split it equally. How many slices will each person receive?

_____

34. The temperature was $-1°F$, $-5°F$, $8°F$, and $-6°F$ on four consecutive days. What was the average temperature for those days?

_____

Holt Mathematics

Name _____ Date _____ Class _____

Determine which value is a solution of the equation.

1. $x - 6 = 12$; $x = 6, 8,$ or 18

2. $9 + x = 17$; $x = 6, 8,$ or 26

_____

_____

3. $x - 12 = 26$; $x = 14, 38,$ or 40

4. $x + 18 = 59$; $x = 37, 41,$ or 77

_____

_____

Solve.

5. $n - 8 = 11$

6. $9 + g = 13$

7. $y + 6 = 2$

_____

_____

_____

8. $-6 + j = -12$

9. $s - 8 = 11$

10. $-16 + r = -2$

_____

_____

_____

11. $a + 35 = 51$

12. $m - 6 = -13$

13. $d - 12 = -5$

_____

_____

_____

14. $7.5 + c = 10.6$

15. $y - 1.7 = 0.6$

16. $m - 2.25 = 4.50$

_____

_____

_____

17. Two sisters, Jenny and Penny, play on the same basketball team. Last season they scored a combined total of 458 points. Jenny scored 192 of the points. Write and solve an equation to find the number of points Penny scored.

_____

18. After his payment, Mr. Weber's credit card balance was $245.76. His payment was for $75.00. Write and solve an equation to find the amount of his credit card bill.

_____

Holt Mathematics

Name _____ Date _____ Class _____

Practice

1-8 *Solving Equations by Multiplying or Dividing*

Solve and check.

1. $4w = 48$

2. $8y = 56$

3. $-4b = 64$

_____

4. $\frac{x}{4} = -9$

5. $\frac{v}{-6} = -14$

6. $\frac{n}{21} = -3$

_____

7. $5a = -75$

8. $54 = 3q$

9. $23b = 161$

_____

10. $\frac{k}{21} = 15$

11. $\frac{w}{-17} = 17$

12. $11 = \frac{r}{34}$

_____

13. $672 = -24b$

14. $\frac{u}{25} = 13$

15. $42m = -966$

_____

16. $3x + 7 = 16$

17. $\frac{t}{5} + 8 = 10$

18. $5 = 2n - 3$

_____

19. Alex scored 13 points in the basketball game. This was $\frac{1}{5}$ of the total points the team scored. Write and solve an equation to determine the total points t the team scored.

_____

20. Jar candles at the Candle Co. cost $4. Nikki spent $92 buying jar candles for party favors. Write and solve an equation to determine how many jar candles c Nikki bought at the Candle Co.

_____

Holt Mathematics

LESSON **Practice**
1-9 *Introduction to Inequalities*

Compare each inequality. Write < or >.

1. $7 + 10$ ☐ 16 **2.** 21 ☐ $4(5)$ **3.** $25 - 7$ ☐ 19

4. 58 ☐ $7(8)$ **5.** $-4(8)$ ☐ -30 **6.** $3 - 8$ ☐ -2

7. $7 + (-7)$ ☐ -17 **8.** $9(-7)$ ☐ -70 **9.** $-43 + (-18)$ ☐ -23

Solve and graph each inequality.

10. $x + 4 > 9$

11. $c - 6 \leq 1$

12. $y + 3 \geq -8$

13. $3 + v < -5$

14. $7 + x \leq 10$

15. $s - 4 < -10$

16. $b - 2 \leq 5$

17. $7 + n > -2$

18. $r + 6 \geq -1$

19. $-9 + w < -15$

20. $14 + k > 25$

21. $a - 8 \geq -12$

22. $k + 3 \leq 0$

23. $n + 6 \geq 2$

24. $-1 + b \leq -1$

Holt Mathematics

Name _____ Date _____ Class _____

Simplify.

1. $\frac{6}{9}$

_____

2. $\frac{48}{96}$

_____

3. $\frac{13}{52}$

_____

4. $-\frac{7}{28}$

_____

5. $\frac{15}{40}$

_____

6. $-\frac{4}{48}$

_____

7. $-\frac{14}{63}$

_____

8. $\frac{12}{72}$

_____

Write each decimal as a fraction in simplest form.

9. 0.72

_____

10. 0.058

_____

11. −1.65

_____

12. 2.1

_____

13. 0.036

_____

14. −4.06

_____

15. 2.305

_____

16. 0.0064

_____

17. −0.60

_____

18. 6.95

_____

19. 0.016

_____

20. 0.0005

_____

Write each fraction as a decimal.

21. $\frac{1}{8}$

_____

22. $\frac{8}{3}$

_____

23. $\frac{14}{15}$

_____

24. $\frac{16}{5}$

_____

25. $\frac{11}{16}$

_____

26. $\frac{7}{9}$

_____

27. $\frac{4}{5}$

_____

28. $\frac{31}{25}$

_____

29. Make up a fraction that cannot be simplified that has 24 as its denominator.

_____

Holt Mathematics

Name _____ Date _____ Class _____

Practice

2-2 *Comparing and Ordering Rational Numbers*

Compare. Write <, >, or =.

1. $\frac{1}{8}$ ☐ $\frac{1}{10}$ 2. $\frac{3}{5}$ ☐ $\frac{7}{10}$ 3. $-\frac{1}{3}$ ☐ $-\frac{3}{4}$

4. $\frac{5}{6}$ ☐ $\frac{3}{4}$ 5. $-\frac{2}{7}$ ☐ $-\frac{1}{2}$ 6. $1\frac{2}{9}$ ☐ $1\frac{2}{3}$

7. $-\frac{8}{9}$ ☐ $-\frac{3}{10}$ 8. $-\frac{4}{5}$ ☐ $-\frac{8}{10}$ 9. 0.08 ☐ $\frac{3}{10}$

10. $\frac{11}{15}$ ☐ $0.7\overline{3}$ 11. $2\frac{4}{9}$ ☐ $2\frac{3}{4}$ 12. $-\frac{5}{8}$ ☐ -0.58

13. $3\frac{1}{4}$ ☐ 3.3   14. $-\frac{1}{6}$ ☐ $-\frac{1}{9}$ 15. 0.75 ☐ $\frac{3}{4}$

16. $-2\frac{1}{8}$ ☐ -2.1 17. $1\frac{1}{2}$ ☐ 1.456   18. $-\frac{3}{5}$ ☐ -0.6

19. On Monday, Gina ran 1 mile in 9.3 minutes. Her times for running 1 mile on each of the next four days, relative to her time on Monday, were $-1\frac{2}{3}$ minutes, -1.45 minutes, -1.8 minutes, and $-1\frac{3}{8}$ minutes. List these relative times in order from least to greatest.

_____

20. Trail A is 3.1 miles long. Trail C is $3\frac{1}{4}$ miles long. Trail B is longer than Trail A but shorter than Trail C. What is a reasonable distance for the length of Trail B?

_____

Holt Mathematics

LESSON **Practice**
2-3 *Adding and Subtracting Rational Numbers*

1. Gretchen bought a sweater for $23.89. In addition, she had to pay $1.43 in sales tax. She gave the sales clerk $30. How much change did Gretchen receive from her total purchase?

2. Jacob is replacing the molding around two sides of a picture frame. The measurements of the sides of the frame are $4\frac{3}{16}$ in. and $2\frac{5}{16}$ in. What length of molding will Jacob need?

_____

Use a number line to find each sum.

3. $-0.5 + 0.4$

_____

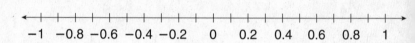

4. $-\frac{2}{7} + \frac{6}{7}$

_____

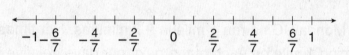

Add or subtract. Simplify.

5. $\frac{3}{8} + \frac{1}{8}$

6. $-\frac{1}{10} + \frac{7}{10}$

7. $\frac{5}{14} - \frac{3}{14}$

8. $\frac{4}{15} + \frac{7}{15}$

_____ _____ _____ _____

9. $\frac{5}{18} - \frac{7}{18}$

10. $-\frac{8}{17} - \frac{2}{17}$

11. $-\frac{1}{16} + \frac{5}{16}$

12. $\frac{3}{20} + \frac{1}{20}$

_____ _____ _____ _____

Evaluate each expression for the given value of the variable.

13. $38.1 + x$ for $x = -6.1$

14. $18.7 + x$ for $x = 8.5$

15. $\frac{8}{15} + x$ for $x = -\frac{4}{15}$

_____ _____ _____

Holt Mathematics

Name _____ Date _____ Class _____

Multiply. Write each answer in simplest form.

1. $8\left(\dfrac{3}{4}\right)$

2. $-6\left(\dfrac{9}{18}\right)$

3. $-9\left(\dfrac{5}{6}\right)$

4. $-6\left(-\dfrac{7}{12}\right)$

_____   _____   _____   _____

5. $-\dfrac{5}{18}\left(\dfrac{8}{15}\right)$

6. $\dfrac{7}{12}\left(\dfrac{14}{21}\right)$

7. $-\dfrac{1}{9}\left(\dfrac{27}{24}\right)$

8. $-\dfrac{1}{11}\left(-\dfrac{3}{2}\right)$

_____   _____   _____   _____

9. $\dfrac{7}{20}\left(-\dfrac{15}{28}\right)$

10. $\dfrac{16}{25}\left(-\dfrac{18}{32}\right)$

11. $\dfrac{1}{9}\left(-\dfrac{18}{17}\right)$

12. $\dfrac{17}{20}\left(-\dfrac{12}{34}\right)$

_____   _____   _____   _____

13. $-4\left(2\dfrac{1}{6}\right)$

14. $\dfrac{3}{4}\left(1\dfrac{3}{8}\right)$

15. $3\dfrac{1}{5}\left(\dfrac{2}{3}\right)$

16. $-\dfrac{5}{6}\left(2\dfrac{1}{2}\right)$

_____   _____   _____   _____

Multiply.

17. $-2(-5.2)$

18. $0.53(0.04)$

19. $(-7)(-3.9)$

20. $-2(8.13)$

_____   _____   _____   _____

21. $0.02(-4.62)$

22. $0.5(-7.8)$

23. $(-0.41)(-8.5)$

24. $(-8)(6.3)$

_____   _____   _____   _____

25. $15(-0.05)$

26. $(-3.04)(-1.7)$

27. $10(-0.09)$

28. $(-0.8)(-0.15)$

_____   _____   _____   _____

29. Travis painted for $6\dfrac{2}{3}$ hours. He received \$27 an hour for his
work. How much was Travis paid for doing this painting job?

_____

13   **Holt Mathematics**

LESSON **Practice**
2-5 *Dividing Rational Numbers*

Divide. Write each answer in simplest form.

1. $\dfrac{1}{5} \div \dfrac{3}{10}$

2. $-\dfrac{5}{8} \div \dfrac{3}{4}$

3. $\dfrac{1}{4} \div \dfrac{1}{8}$

4. $-\dfrac{2}{3} \div \dfrac{4}{15}$

_____ _____ _____ _____

5. $1\dfrac{2}{9} \div 1\dfrac{2}{3}$

6. $-\dfrac{7}{10} \div \left(\dfrac{2}{5}\right)$

7. $\dfrac{6}{11} \div \dfrac{3}{22}$

8. $\dfrac{4}{9} \div \left(-\dfrac{8}{15}\right)$

_____ _____ _____ _____

9. $\dfrac{3}{8} \div -15$

10. $-\dfrac{5}{6} \div 12$

11. $6\dfrac{1}{2} \div 1\dfrac{5}{8}$

12. $-\dfrac{9}{10} \div 6$

_____ _____ _____ _____

Divide.

13. $24.35 \div 0.5$

14. $2.16 \div 0.04$

15. $3.16 \div 0.02$

16. $7.32 \div 0.3$

_____ _____ _____ _____

17. $87.36 \div 0.6$

18. $79.36 \div 0.8$

19. $4.27 \div 0.007$

20. $63.81 \div 0.9$

_____ _____ _____ _____

21. $1.23 \div 0.003$

22. $62.46 \div 0.09$

23. $21.12 \div 0.4$

24. $82.68 \div 0.06$

_____ _____ _____ _____

Evaluate each expression for the given value of the variable.

25. $\dfrac{18}{x}$ for $x = 0.12$

26. $\dfrac{10.8}{x}$ for $x = 0.03$

27. $\dfrac{9.18}{x}$ for $x = -1.2$

_____ _____ _____

28. A can of fruit contains $3\dfrac{1}{2}$ cups of fruit. The suggested serving
size is $\dfrac{1}{2}$ cup. How many servings are in the can of fruit?

_____

Holt Mathematics

LESSON **Practice**

2-6 *Adding and Subtracting with Unlike Denominators*

Add or subtract.

1. $\frac{2}{3} + \frac{1}{2}$

2. $\frac{3}{5} + \frac{1}{3}$

3. $\frac{3}{4} - \frac{1}{3}$

4. $\frac{1}{2} - \frac{5}{9}$

_____ _____ _____ _____

5. $\frac{5}{16} - \frac{5}{8}$

6. $\frac{7}{9} + \frac{5}{6}$

7. $\frac{7}{8} - \frac{1}{4}$

8. $\frac{5}{6} - \frac{3}{8}$

_____ _____ _____ _____

9. $2\frac{7}{8} + 3\frac{5}{12}$

10. $1\frac{2}{9} + 2\frac{1}{18}$

11. $3\frac{2}{3} - 1\frac{3}{5}$

12. $1\frac{5}{6} + \left(-2\frac{3}{4}\right)$

_____ _____ _____ _____

13. $8\frac{1}{3} - 3\frac{5}{9}$

14. $5\frac{1}{3} + 1\frac{11}{12}$

15. $7\frac{1}{4} + \left(-2\frac{5}{12}\right)$

16. $5\frac{2}{5} - 7\frac{3}{10}$

_____ _____ _____ _____

Evaluate each expression for the given value of the variable.

17. $2\frac{3}{8} + x$ for $x = 1\frac{5}{6}$

18. $x - \frac{2}{5}$ for $x = \frac{1}{3}$

19. $x - \frac{3}{10}$ for $x = \frac{3}{7}$

_____ _____ _____

20. $1\frac{5}{8} + x$ for $x = -2\frac{1}{6}$

21. $x - \frac{3}{4}$ for $x = \frac{1}{6}$

22. $x - \frac{3}{10}$ for $x = \frac{1}{2}$

_____ _____ _____

23. Ana worked $6\frac{1}{2}$ h on Monday, $5\frac{3}{4}$ h on Tuesday and $7\frac{1}{6}$ h on Friday. How many total hours did she work these three days?

_____

Holt Mathematics

LESSON 2-7

Practice
Solving Equations with Rational Numbers

Solve.

1. $x + 6.8 = 12.19$

2. $y - 10.24 = 5.3$

3. $0.05w = 6.25$

_____

_____

_____

4. $\dfrac{a}{9.05} = 8.2$

5. $-12.41 + x = -0.06$

6. $\dfrac{d}{-8.4} = -10.2$

_____

_____

_____

7. $-2.89 = 1.7m$

8. $n - 8.09 = -11.65$

9. $\dfrac{x}{5.4} = -7.18$

_____

_____

_____

10. $\dfrac{7}{9} + x = 1\dfrac{1}{9}$

11. $\dfrac{6}{11}y = -\dfrac{18}{22}$

12. $\dfrac{7}{10}d = \dfrac{21}{20}$

_____

_____

_____

13. $x - \left(-\dfrac{9}{14}\right) = \dfrac{5}{7}$

14. $x - \dfrac{15}{21} = 2\dfrac{6}{7}$

15. $-\dfrac{8}{15}a = \dfrac{9}{10}$

_____

_____

_____

16. A recipe calls for $2\dfrac{1}{3}$ cups of flour and $1\dfrac{1}{4}$ cups of sugar. If the recipe is tripled, how much flour and sugar will be needed?

_____

17. Daniel filled the gas tank in his car with 14.6 gal of gas. He then drove 284.7 mi before needing to fill up his tank with gas again. How many miles did the car get to a gallon of gasoline?

_____

Holt Mathematics

Name _____ Date _____ Class _____

Solving Two-Step Equations

Write and solve a two-step equation to answer the following questions.

1. The school purchased baseball equipment and uniforms for a total cost of $1762. The equipment costs $598 and the uniforms were $24.25 each. How many uniforms did the school purchase?

2. Carla runs 4 miles every day. She jogs from home to the school track, which is $\frac{3}{4}$ mile away. She then runs laps around the $\frac{1}{4}$-mile track. Carla then jogs home. How many laps does she run at the school?

_____

_____

_____

_____

_____

Solve.

3. $\frac{a+5}{3} = 12$

4. $\frac{x+2}{4} = -2$

5. $\frac{y-4}{6} = -3$

6. $\frac{k+1}{8} = 7$

_____   _____   _____   _____

7. $0.5x - 6 = -4$

8. $\frac{x}{2} + 3 = -4$

9. $\frac{1}{5}n + 3 = 6$

10. $2a - 7 = -9$

_____   _____   _____   _____

11. $\frac{3x-1}{4} = 2$

12. $-7.8 = 4.4 + 2r$

13. $\frac{-4w+5}{-3} = -7$

14. $1.3 - 5r = 7.4$

_____   _____   _____   _____

15. A phone call costs $0.58 for the first 3 minutes and $0.15 for each additional minute. If the total charge for the call was $4.78, how many minutes was the call? _____

16. Seventeen less than four times a number is twenty-seven. Find the number. _____

Holt Mathematics

LESSON 3-1 Practice
Ordered Pairs

Determine whether each ordered pair is a solution of $y = 4 + 2x$.

1. (1, 1)   **2.** (2, 8)   **3.** (0, 4)   **4.** (8, 2)

_____   _____   _____   _____

Determine whether each ordered pair is a solution of $y = 3x - 2$.

5. (1, 1)   **6.** (3, 7)   **7.** (5, 15)   **8.** (6, 16)

_____   _____   _____   _____

Use the given values to complete the table of solutions.

9. $y = x + 5$ for $x = 0, 1, 2, 3, 4$

x	x + 5	y	(x, y)
0			
1			
2			
3			
4			

10. $y = 3x + 1$ for $x = 1, 2, 3, 4, 5$

x	3x + 1	y	(x, y)
1			
2			
3			
4			
5			

11. $y = 2x + 6$ for $x = 0, 1, 2, 3, 4$

x	2x + 6	y	(x, y)
0			
1			
2			
3			
4			

12. $y = 4x - 2$ for $x = 2, 4, 6, 8, 10$

x	4x - 2	y	(x, y)
2			
4			
6			
8			
10			

13. Alexis opened a savings account with a $120 deposit. Each week she will put $20 into the account. The equation that gives the total amount t in her account is $t = 120 + 20w$, where w is the number of weeks since she opened the account. How much money will Alexis have in her savings account after 5 weeks?

_____

Holt Mathematics

LESSON 3-2 Practice
Graphing on a Coordinate Plane

Give the coordinates of each point and quadrant.

1. F

_____

2. X

_____

3. T

_____

4. B

_____

5. D

_____

6. R

_____

7. H

_____

8. Y

_____

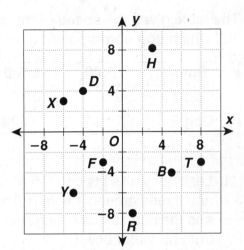

Graph each point on a coordinate plane.

9. $A(2\frac{1}{2}, 1)$

10. $B(0, 4)$

11. $C(2, -1.5)$

12. $D(-2, 3.5)$

13. $E(-2\frac{1}{3}, 0)$

14. $F(-1\frac{1}{2}, -3)$

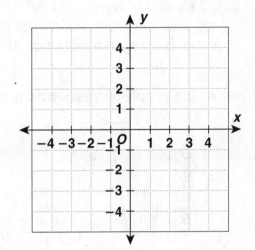

Complete the table of ordered pairs. Graph each ordered pair on a coordinate plane. Draw a line through the points.

15. $y = 1\frac{1}{2}x$

x	$1\frac{1}{2}x$	y	(x, y)
0			
1			
2			

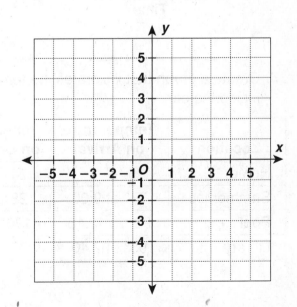

Holt Mathematics

LESSON **Practice**
3-3 *Interpreting Graphs and Tables*

The table gives the speed of three dogs in mi/h at the given times.
Tell which dog corresponds to each situation described below.

Time	5:00	5:01	5:02	5:03	5:04
Dog 1	0	1	12	0	0
Dog 2	5	23	4	0	0
Dog 3	14	0	18	2	9

1. Leshaan walks his dog. Then he lets the dog off the leash and it runs around the yard. Then they go into the house and the dog stands eating from his dog dish and drinking from his water bowl.

   _____

2. Luke's dog is chasing its tail. Then it stops and pants. The dog then runs to the backyard fence and walks along the fence, barking at a neighbor. Then it runs to Luke at the back door.

   _____

Tell which graph corresponds to each situation in Exercises 1–2.

3.
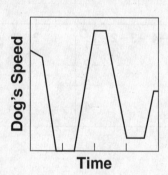

4.
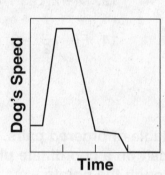

_____   _____

5. Create a graph that illustrates the temperature inside the car.

Location	Temperature on Arrival	Temperature on Departure
Home	—	74° at 8:30
Summer job	77° at 9:00	128° at 12:05
Pool	92° at 12:15	136° at 2:30
Library	95° at 2:40	77° at 5:10

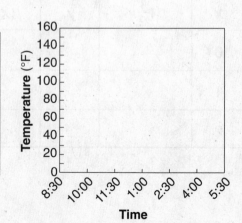

Holt Mathematics

Name _____ Date _____ Class _____

LESSON 3-4 Practice
Functions

Complete the table and graph each function.

1. $y = -2x + 5$

x	−2x + 5	y
−2		
−1		
0		
1		
2		

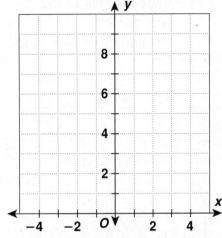

2. $y = x - 2$

x	x − 2	y
−2		
−1		
0		
1		
2		

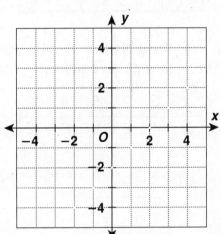

Determine if each relationship represents a function.

3. $y = \frac{1}{3}x - \frac{2}{5}$

4.

x	1	2	1	2
y	6	5	−6	−5

5.

x	y
0	0
1	−1
2	−8
3	−27
4	−64

6.

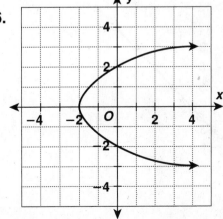

Holt Mathematics

Name _____ Date _____ Class _____

Practice

Equations, Tables, and Graphs

1. The amount of water in a tank being filled is represented by the equation $g = 20m$, where g is the number of gallons in the tank after m minutes. Make a table and sketch a graph of the equation.

m	$20m$	g
0		
1		
2		
3		
4		

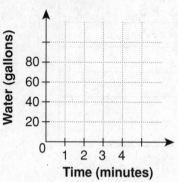

2. Use the table to make a graph and to write an equation.

x	0	2	5	8	12
y	4	6	9	12	16

_____

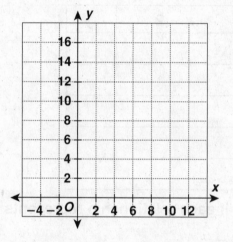

3. Use the graph to make a table and to write an equation.

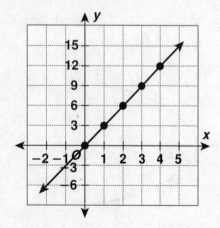

x				
y				

_____

Holt Mathematics

Name _____ Date _____ Class _____

Find the common difference in each arithmetic sequence.

1. 5, 9, 13, 17, …   **2.** 3, 10, 17, 24, …   **3.** 35, 32, 29, 26, …

_____   _____   _____

4. 6, 15, 24, 33, …   **5.** 92, 87, 82, 77, …   **6.** 60, 54, 48, 42, …

_____   _____   _____

7. 108, 96, 84, 72, …   **8.** 3.8, 4, 4.2, 4.4, …   **9.** 95, 88, 81, 74, …

_____   _____   _____

Find the next three terms in each arithmetic sequence.

10. 12, 18, 24, 30, …   **11.** $1\frac{1}{2}$, 2, $2\frac{1}{2}$, 3, …   **12.** −7, −14, −21, −28, …

_____   _____   _____

13. 0.5, 1, 1.5, 2, …   **14.** −8, −16, −24, −32, …   **15.** 72, 63, 54, 45, …

_____   _____   _____

16. 3.5, 7, 10.5, 14, …   **17.** $\frac{1}{3}$, $\frac{2}{3}$, 1, $1\frac{1}{3}$, …   **18.** 10, 9.5, 9, 8.5, …

_____   _____   _____

**Find a function that describes each arithmetic sequence. Use *y*
to identify each term in the sequence and *n* to identify each
term's position.**

19. 6, 12, 18, 24, …   **20.** −8, −16, −24, −32, …   **21.** 12, 24, 36, 48, …

_____   _____   _____

22. It costs $12 to rent a mini-car to go around the track, plus $4 per
lap. Find a function that describes the sequence. Then find the
total cost of driving 5 laps around the track.

_____

23   **Holt Mathematics**

Name _____ Date _____ Class _____

Write in exponential form.

1. $6 \cdot 6 \cdot 6 \cdot 6 \cdot 6 \cdot 6$

_____

2. $7 \cdot 7 \cdot 7 \cdot 7$

_____

3. $(-8) \cdot (-8) \cdot (-8) \cdot (-8)$

_____

4. $5 \cdot 5 \cdot 5 \cdot b \cdot b \cdot b \cdot b$

_____

Evaluate.

5. 10^2

_____

6. $(-6)^2$

_____

7. 8^2

_____

8. $(-7)^2$

_____

9. $(-5)^3$

_____

10. 12^2

_____

11. $(-9)^2$

_____

12. $(-4)^3$

_____

13. 2^5

_____

14. 5^4

_____

15. $(-3)^4$

_____

16. 6^3

_____

Evaluate each expression for the given values of the variables.

17. $n^3 - 5$ for $n = 4$

_____

18. $4x^2 + y^3$ for $x = 5$ and $y = -2$

_____

19. $m^p + q^2$ for $m = 5$, $p = 2$, and $q = 4$

_____

20. $a^4 + 2(b - c^2)$ for $a = 2$, $b = 4$, and $c = -1$

_____

21. Write an expression for five times a number used as a factor three times.

_____

22. Find the volume of a regular cube if the length of a side is 10 cm. (Hint: $V = l^3$.)

_____

Holt Mathematics

LESSON | Practice
4-2 *Look for a Pattern in Integer Exponents*

Evaluate the powers of 10.

1. 10^{-3} **2.** 10^3 **3.** 10^{-5} **4.** 10^{-2}

_____   _____   _____   _____

5. 10^0 **6.** 10^4 **7.** 10^1 **8.** 10^5

_____   _____   _____   _____

Evaluate.

9. $(-6)^{-2}$ **10.** $(-9)^{-3}$ **11.** 2^{-5}

_____   _____   _____

12. $(-3)^{-4}$ **13.** $(-12)^{-1}$ **14.** 6^{-3}

_____   _____   _____

15. $10 - (3 + 2)^0 + 2^{-1}$ **16.** $15 + (-6)^0 - 3^{-2}$

_____   _____

17. $6(8 - 2)^0 + 4^{-2}$ **18.** $2^{-2} + (-4)^{-1}$

_____   _____

19. $3(1 - 4)^{-2} + 9^{-1} + 12^0$ **20.** $9^0 + 64(3 + 5)^{-2}$

_____   _____

21. One milliliter equals 10^{-3} liter. Evaluate 10^{-3}.

_____

22. The volume of a cube is 10^6 cubic feet. Evaluate 10^6.

_____

Name _____ Date _____ Class _____

Practice
4-3 *Properties of Exponents*

Multiply. Write the product as one power.

1. $10^5 \cdot 10^7$ **2.** $x^9 \cdot x^8$ **3.** $14^7 \cdot 14^9$ **4.** $12^6 \cdot 12^8$

_____   _____   _____   _____

5. $y^{12} \cdot y^{10}$ **6.** $15^9 \cdot 15^{14}$ **7.** $(-11)^{20} \cdot (-11)^{10}$ **8.** $(-a)^6 \cdot (-a)^7$

_____   _____   _____   _____

Divide. Write the quotient as one power.

9. $\dfrac{12^9}{12^2}$ **10.** $\dfrac{(-11)^{12}}{(-11)^8}$ **11.** $\dfrac{x^{10}}{x^5}$ **12.** $\dfrac{16^{10}}{16^2}$

_____   _____   _____   _____

13. $\dfrac{17^{19}}{17^2}$ **14.** $\dfrac{14^{15}}{14^{13}}$ **15.** $\dfrac{23^{17}}{23^9}$ **16.** $\dfrac{(-a)^{12}}{(-a)^7}$

_____   _____   _____   _____

Simplify.

17. $(6^2)^4$ **18.** $(2^4)^{-3}$ **19.** $(3^5)^{-1}$ **20.** $(y^5)^2$

_____   _____   _____   _____

21. $(9^{-2})^3$ **22.** $(10^0)^3$ **23.** $(x^4)^{-2}$ **24.** $(5^{-2})^0$

_____   _____   _____   _____

Write the product or quotient as one power.

25. $\dfrac{w^{12}}{w^3}$ **26.** $d^8 \cdot d^5$ **27.** $(-15)^5 \cdot (-15)^{10}$

_____   _____   _____

28. Jefferson High School has a student body of 6^4 students. Each class has approximately 6^2 students. How many classes does the school have? Write the answer as one power.

_____

29. Write the expression for a number used as a factor fifteen times being multiplied by a number used as a factor ten times. Then, write the product as one power.

_____

Holt Mathematics

Name _____ Date _____ Class _____

Write each number in standard notation.

1. 2.54×10^2 **2.** 6.7×10^{-2} **3.** 1.14×10^3 **4.** 3.8×10^{-1}

_____   _____   _____   _____

5. 7.53×10^{-3} **6.** 5.6×10^4 **7.** 9.1×10^5 **8.** 6.08×10^{-4}

_____   _____   _____   _____

9. 8.59×10^5 **10.** 3.331×10^6 **11.** 7.21×10^{-3} **12.** 5.88×10^{-4}

_____   _____   _____   _____

Write each number in scientific notation.

13. 75,000,000   **14.** 208   **15.** 907,100

_____   _____   _____

16. 56   **17.** 0.093   **18.** 0.00006

_____   _____   _____

19. 0.00852   **20.** 0.0505   **21.** 0.003007

_____   _____   _____

22. 5226   **23.** 0.04   **24.** 98,856

_____   _____   _____

25. Jupiter is about 778,120,000 kilometers from the Sun. Write this number in scientific notation.

_____

26. The *E. coli* bacterium is about 5×10^{-7} meters wide. A hair is about 1.7×10^{-5} meters wide. Which is wider, the bacterium or the hair?

_____

Holt Mathematics

Name _____ Date _____ Class _____

Practice

4-5 *Squares and Square Roots*

Find the two square roots of each number.

1. 36   **2.** 81   **3.** 49   **4.** 100

_____   _____   _____   _____

5. 64   **6.** 121   **7.** 25   **8.** 144

_____   _____   _____   _____

Evaluate each expression.

9. $\sqrt{32 + 17}$ **10.** $\sqrt{100 - 19}$ **11.** $\sqrt{64 + 36}$ **12.** $\sqrt{73 - 48}$

_____   _____   _____   _____

13. $2\sqrt{64} + 10$ **14.** $36 - \sqrt{36}$ **15.** $\sqrt{100} - \sqrt{25}$ **16.** $\sqrt{121} + 16$

_____   _____   _____   _____

17. $\sqrt{\dfrac{25}{4}} + \dfrac{1}{2}$ **18.** $\sqrt{\dfrac{100}{25}}$ **19.** $\sqrt{\dfrac{196}{49}}$ **20.** $3(\sqrt{144} - 6)$

_____   _____   _____   _____

The Pyramids of Egypt are often called the first wonder of the world.
This group of pyramids consists of Menkaura, Khufu, and Khafra.
The largest of these is Khufu, sometimes called Cheops. During this
time in history, each monarch had his own pyramid built to bury his
mummified body. Cheops was a king of Egypt in the early 26th
century B.C. His pyramid's original height is estimated to have been
482 ft. It is now approximately 450 ft. The estimated completion
date of this structure was 2660 B.C.

21. If the area of the base of Cheops' pyramid is 570,025 ft², what is
the length of one of the sides of the ancient structure?
(Hint: $s = \sqrt{A}$)

_____

22. If a replica of the pyramid were built with a base area of
625 in², what would be the length of each side?
(Hint: $s = \sqrt{A}$)

_____

Holt Mathematics

Name _____ Date _____ Class _____

Each square root is between two integers. Name the integers.
Explain your answer.

1. $\sqrt{6}$

2. $\sqrt{20}$

_____   _____

3. $\sqrt{28}$

4. $\sqrt{44}$

_____   _____

5. $\sqrt{31}$

6. $\sqrt{52}$

_____   _____

Use a calculator to find each value. Round to the nearest tenth.

7. $\sqrt{14}$ 8. $\sqrt{42}$ 9. $\sqrt{21}$ 10. $\sqrt{47}$

_____   _____   _____   _____

11. $\sqrt{58}$ 12. $\sqrt{60}$ 13. $\sqrt{35}$ 14. $\sqrt{75}$

_____   _____   _____   _____

Police use the formula $r = 2\sqrt{5L}$ to approximate the rate of speed
in miles per hours of a vehicle from its skid marks, where L is the
length of the skid marks in feet.

15. About how fast is a car going that leaves skid marks of 80 ft?

_____

16. About how fast is a car going that leaves skid marks of 245 ft?

_____

17. If the formula for finding the length of the skid marks is $L = \dfrac{r^2}{20}$,
  what would be the length of the skid marks from a vehicle
  traveling 80 mi/h?

_____

Holt Mathematics

Name _____ Date _____ Class _____

Practice
The Real Numbers

Write all names that apply to each number.

1. $-\dfrac{7}{8}$

_____

_____

2. $\sqrt{0.15}$

_____

_____

3. $\sqrt{\dfrac{18}{2}}$

_____

_____

4. $\sqrt{45}$

_____

_____

5. -25

_____

_____

6. -6.75

_____

_____

State if the number is rational, irrational, or not a real number.

7. $\sqrt{14}$

_____

8. $\sqrt{-16}$

_____

9. $\dfrac{6.2}{0}$

_____

10. $\sqrt{49}$

_____

11. $\dfrac{7}{20}$

_____

12. $-\sqrt{81}$

_____

13. $\sqrt{\dfrac{7}{9}}$

_____

14. -1.3

_____

Find a real number between each pair of numbers.

15. $7\dfrac{3}{5}$ and $7\dfrac{4}{5}$

16. 6.45 and $\dfrac{13}{2}$

17. $\dfrac{7}{8}$ and $\dfrac{9}{10}$

_____

18. Give an example of a rational number between $-\sqrt{4}$ and $\sqrt{4}$

_____

19. Give an example of an irrational number less than 0.

_____

20. Give an example of a number that is not real.

_____

Holt Mathematics

Name _____ Date _____ Class _____

Find the length of the hypotenuse to the nearest tenth.

1.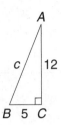

_____

2.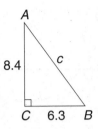

_____

3.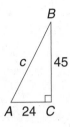

_____

Solve for the unknown side in each right triangle to the nearest tenth.

4.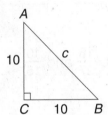

_____

5.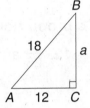

_____

6.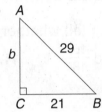

_____

7.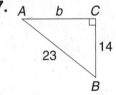

_____

8.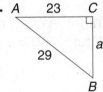

_____

9.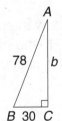

_____

10. A glider flies 8 miles south from the airport and then 15 miles east. Then it flies in a straight line back to the airport. What was the distance of the glider's last leg back to the airport?

_____

Holt Mathematics

Name _____ Date _____ Class _____

Practice
Ratios and Proportions

Find two ratios that are equivalent to each given ratio.

1. $\frac{9}{12}$ 2. $\frac{4}{20}$ 3. $\frac{15}{25}$

_____   _____   _____

4. $\frac{7}{12}$ 5. $\frac{14}{7}$ 6. $\frac{11}{22}$

_____   _____   _____

7. $\frac{10}{3}$ 8. $\frac{18}{28}$ 9. $\frac{12}{27}$

_____   _____   _____

Simplify to tell whether the ratios form a proportion.

10. $\frac{13}{39}$ and $\frac{16}{48}$ 11. $\frac{21}{49}$ and $\frac{28}{56}$ 12. $\frac{12}{28}$ and $\frac{18}{42}$ 13. $\frac{18}{27}$ and $\frac{10}{15}$

_____   _____   _____   _____

14. $\frac{24}{27}$ and $\frac{27}{30}$ 15. $\frac{14}{10}$ and $\frac{35}{25}$ 16. $\frac{10}{32}$ and $\frac{25}{80}$ 17. $\frac{16}{48}$ and $\frac{15}{45}$

_____   _____   _____   _____

18. Mrs. Walters wanted one daffodil plant for every 2 tulip plants in her garden. If she planted 20 daffodil bulbs, how many tulip bulbs did she plant?

_____

19. In a survey, 9 out of 10 doctors recommended a certain medicine. If 80 doctors were surveyed, how many doctors recommended the medicine?

_____

20. A molecule of sodium carbonate contains 2 atoms of sodium to every 3 atoms of oxygen. Could a compound containing 12 atoms of sodium and 15 atoms of oxygen be sodium carbonate? Explain.

_____

Holt Mathematics

Name _____ Date _____ Class _____

Practice

5-2 *Ratios, Rates, and Unit Rates*

1. Copper weighing 4480 kilograms has a volume of 0.5 cubic meters. What is the density of copper?

   _____

2. Yoshi's yogurt contains 15 calories per ounce. How many calories are in an 8-ounce container of Yoshi's yogurt?

   _____

3. Emily earns $7.50 per hour. How much does she earn in 3 hours?

   _____

Estimate the unit rate.

4. 43 apples in 5 bags

   _____

5. $71.00 for 8 hours

   _____

6. 146 students in 6 classes

   _____

7. $52.00 for 5 hours

   _____

8. 7 miles in 64 minutes

   _____

9. $3.55 for 4 pounds

   _____

Determine the better buy.

10. 8.2 oz of toothpaste for $2.99 or 6.4 oz of toothpaste for $2.49

   _____

11. a 3 lb bag of apples for $2.99 or a 5 lb bag of apples for $4.99

   _____

12. 16 oz bottle of soda for $1.25 or 20 oz bottle of soda for $1.55

   _____

13. Mavis rides the bus every day. She bought a bus pass good for the month of October for $38.75. How much was Mavis charged per day for the bus pass?

   _____

Holt Mathematics

Name _____ Date _____ Class _____

Find the appropriate factor for each conversion.

1. grams to kilograms

2. quarts to gallons

3. minutes to seconds

_____   _____   _____

4. David takes 300 milligrams of medicine every day. How many grams is this?

_____

5. Jody runs the 500-yard dash for his school's track team. How many feet does he run in each 500-yard dash?

_____

6. Sean drinks six 12-ounce cans of soda a week. How many pints of soda does he drink in a week?

_____

7. A recipe for punch requires diluting the punch concentrate with 7 quarts of water. How many gallons of water are required to dilute the concentrate according to the directions?

_____

8. Jesse's dog Angel weighs $18\frac{1}{2}$ pounds. How many ounces does Angel weigh?

_____

9. A roll of tape contains 32.9 meters of tape. How many millimeters of tape does the roll contain?

_____

10. There are two types of lifts in the sport of weightlifting, the *snatch* and the *clean and jerk*. Winners are determined by the combined weights of the two type of lifts. In the 2002 Collegiate Weightlifting Competition, Timothy Leancu from the U.S. Naval Academy competed in the 94-kilogram weight class. He lifted 100 kg in the *snatch* and 132.5 kg in the *clean and jerk*. What was the combined weight of his lifts in grams?

_____

Holt Mathematics

Name _____ Date _____ Class _____

LESSON

Practice

5-4 *Solving Proportions*

Tell whether the ratios are proportional.

1. $\frac{3}{4} \overset{?}{=} \frac{9}{12}$

2. $\frac{9}{24} \overset{?}{=} \frac{18}{48}$

3. $\frac{16}{24} \overset{?}{=} \frac{10}{18}$

4. $\frac{13}{25} \overset{?}{=} \frac{26}{50}$

_____

_____

_____

_____

5. $\frac{10}{32} \overset{?}{=} \frac{16}{38}$

6. $\frac{20}{36} \overset{?}{=} \frac{50}{90}$

7. $\frac{20}{28} \overset{?}{=} \frac{28}{36}$

8. $\frac{14}{42} \overset{?}{=} \frac{16}{36}$

_____

_____

_____

_____

Solve each proportion.

9. $\frac{\$d}{3 \text{ CDs}} = \frac{\$64.75}{5 \text{ CDs}}$

10. $\frac{c \text{ chairs}}{7 \text{ rows}} = \frac{252 \text{ chairs}}{9 \text{ rows}}$

_____

_____

11. $\frac{m \text{ miles}}{5 \text{ hours}} = \frac{135 \text{ miles}}{3 \text{ hours}}$

12. $\frac{\$d}{4 \text{ subs}} = \frac{\$45}{10 \text{ subs}}$

_____

_____

Solve each proportional situation using equivalent fractions.

13. $\frac{c}{15} = \frac{4}{10}$

14. $\frac{a}{6} = \frac{8}{12}$

15. $\frac{b}{20} = \frac{15}{12}$

16. $\frac{w}{6} = \frac{15}{10}$

_____

_____

_____

_____

17. Janessa bought 4 stamps for $1.48. At this rate, how much would 10 stamps cost?

18. A karate team had 6 girls and 9 boys. Then 2 more girls and 3 more boys joined the team. Did the ratio of girls to boys stay the same? Explain.

19. A 30 kg weight is positioned 2 m from a fulcrum. At what distance from the fulcrum must a 40 kg weight be positioned to keep the scale balanced?

35

Holt Mathematics

LESSON Practice
5-5 *Similar Figures*

1. Are any of these triangles similar?

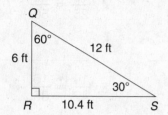 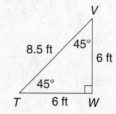 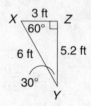

_____

2. A photo is 12 in. wide by 18 in. tall. If the width is
scaled down to 9 inches, how tall should the
similar photo be?   _____

3. An isosceles triangle has a base of 20 cm
and legs measuring 36 cm. How long are the legs
of a similar triangle with base measuring 50 cm?   _____

4. A picture of a school's mascot is 18 in. wide and 24 in.
long. It is enlarged proportionally to banner size. If
the width is enlarged to 63 in., what is the length of
the banner?   _____

5. Carol has a 24 cm × 36 cm photo that she reduces
to $\frac{3}{4}$ of its size. What are the dimensions of the
new photo?   _____

6. Erik is drawing a picture of his school's basketball
court. The actual basketball court is 84 ft long and
50 ft wide. If Erik draws the court with a length of
21 in., what will be the width?   _____

7. IMAX theaters have the world's largest screens.
There are numerous IMAX theaters around the world.
The Henry Ford Museum in Dearborn, Michigan
hosts an IMAX theater with a 60 ft × 84 ft screen.
If a classroom projection screen were changed to
be in direct proportion with the IMAX screen at the
Henry Ford Museum, the dimensions
would be 5 ft × ___ ft.   _____

Holt Mathematics

Name _____ Date _____ Class _____

Tell whether each transformation is a dilation.

1.
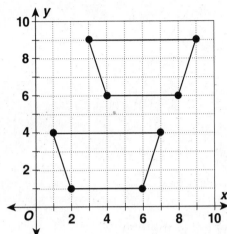

_____

2.
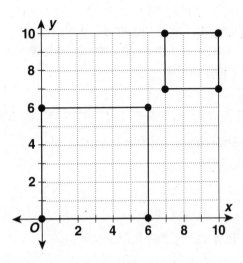

_____

Dilate each figure by the given scale factor with the origin as the center of dilation. What are the vertices of the image?

3. scale factor of 2

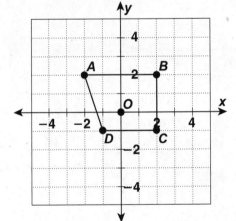

_____

_____

4. scale factor of $\frac{1}{2}$

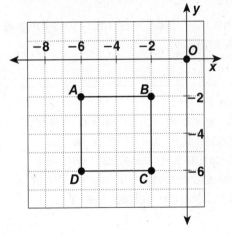

_____

_____

Holt Mathematics

Practice
5-7 *Indirect Measurement*

1. Tamara wants to know the width of the pond at the park. She drew the diagram and labeled it with the measurements she made. How wide is the pond?

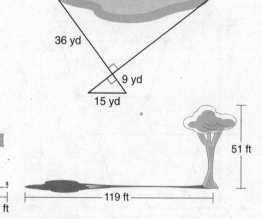

_____

Use the diagram for 2 and 3.

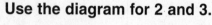

2. How tall is the flagpole?

3. How tall is the child?

_____   _____

Use the diagram for 4 and 5.

4. How tall is the house?

_____

5. The tree is 56 feet tall. How long is its shadow?

_____

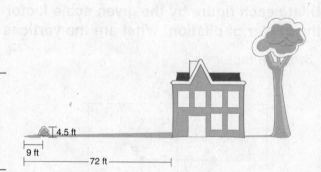

6. Drew wants to know the distance across the river. He drew the diagram and labeled it with the measurements he made. What is the distance across the river?

_____

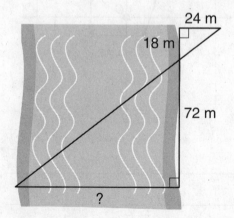

7. A warehouse is 120 feet tall and casts a shadow 288 feet long. At the same time, Julie casts a shadow 12 feet long. How tall is Julie?

_____

Holt Mathematics

Name _____ Date _____ Class _____

The scale of a drawing is $\frac{1}{4}$ in. = 15 ft. Find the actual measurement.

1. 9 in.   **2.** 12 in.   **3.** 14 in.   **4.** 15 in.

_____   _____   _____   _____

The scale is 2 cm = 25 m. Find the length each measurement would be on a scale drawing.

5. 150 m   **6.** 475 m   **7.** 350 m   **8.** 500 m

_____   _____   _____   _____

Tell whether each scale reduces, enlarges, or preserves the size of an actual object.

9. 1 m : 25 cm   **10.** 8 in. : 1 ft   **11.** 12 in. : 1 ft

_____   _____   _____

12. On a map the distance between Atlanta, Georgia, and Nashville, Tennessee, is 12.5 in. The actual distance between these two cities is 250 miles. What is the scale?

_____

13. Blueprints of a house are drawn to the scale of $\frac{1}{4}$ in. = 1 ft. A kitchen measures 3.5 in. by 5 in. on the blueprints. What is the actual size of the kitchen?

_____

14. A scale model of a house is 1 ft long. The actual house is 50 ft long. In the model, the window is $1\frac{1}{5}$ in. high. How many feet high is the actual window?

_____

15. A model of a skyscraper is 1.6 in. long, 2.8 in. wide, and 11.2 in. high. The scale factor is 8 in. : 250 ft. What are the actual dimensions of the skyscraper?

_____

39   **Holt Mathematics**

LESSON 6-1 Practice

Relating Decimals, Fractions, and Percents

Find the missing ratio or percent equivalent for each letter on the number line.

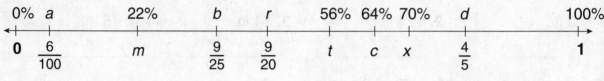

0% *a*   22%   *b*   *r*   56% 64% 70%   *d*   100%

0   $\frac{6}{100}$ *m* $\frac{9}{25}$ $\frac{9}{20}$ *t*   *c*   *x* $\frac{4}{5}$ 1

1. *a*

2. *b*

3. *c*

4. *d*

_____   _____   _____   _____

5. *m*

6. *r*

7. *t*

8. *x*

_____   _____   _____   _____

Compare. Write <, >, or =.

9. $\frac{3}{4}$ ☐ 70%

10. 60% ☐ $\frac{3}{5}$

11. 58% ☐ 0.6

12. 0.09 ☐ 15%

13. $\frac{2}{3}$ ☐ 59%

14. 0.45 ☐ 40.5%

Order the numbers from least to greatest.

15. 99%, 0.95, $\frac{5}{9}$, 9.5%

16. $\frac{3}{8}$, 50%, 0.35, 38%

_____   _____

17. $\frac{4}{5}$, 54%, 0.45, 44.5%

18. $\frac{1}{3}$, 20%, 0.3, 3%

_____   _____

19. There are 25 students in math class. Yesterday, 6 students
were absent. What percent of the students were absent? _____

20. Albert spends 2 hours a day on his homework and an hour
playing video games. What percent of the day is this? _____

21. Ragu ran the first 3 miles of a 5 mile race in 24 minutes.
What percent of the race has he run? _____

Holt Mathematics

LESSON 6-2 **Practice**
Estimate with Percents

Estimate.

1. 74% of 99

2. 25% of 39

3. 52% of 10

_____   _____   _____

4. 21% of 50

5. 30% of 61

6. 24% of 48

_____   _____   _____

7. 5% of 41

8. 50% of 178

9. 33% out of 62

_____   _____   _____

Estimate.

10. 48% of 30 is about what number?

11. 26% of 36 is about what number?

_____   _____

12. 30% of 22 is about what number?

13. 21% of 63 is about what number?

_____   _____

14. Rodney's weekly gross pay is $91. He must pay about
32% in taxes and deductions. Estimate Rodney's weekly
take-home pay after deductions. _____

15. In the last school election, 492 students voted. Mary
received 48% of the votes. About how many votes
did she receive? _____

16. A restaurant bill for lunch is $14.10. Grace wants to leave
a 15% tip and the sales tax rate is 5.5%. About how much
will lunch cost Grace in all? _____

17. A company has found that on average about 6% of the
batteries they manufacture are defective. Out of 1,385
batteries, the supervisor assumes that about 83 are
defective. Estimate to determine if the manager's number
is reasonable? Explain. _____

_____

_____

Holt Mathematics

LESSON 6-3 Practice
Finding Percents

Find each percent.

1. What percent of 84 is 21?

_____

2. 24 is what percent of 60?

_____

3. What percent of 150 is 75?

_____

4. What percent of 80 is 68?

_____

5. 36 is what percent of 80?

_____

6. What percent of 88 is 33?

_____

7. 19 is what percent of 95?

_____

8. 28.8 is what percent of 120?

_____

9. What percent of 56 is 49?

_____

10. What percent of 102 is 17?

_____

11. What percent of 94 is 42.3?

_____

12. 90 is what percent of 75?

_____

13. Daphne bought a used car for $9200. She made a down payment of $1840. Find the percent of the purchase price that is the down payment.   _____

14. Tricia read $\frac{1}{4}$ of her book on Monday. On Tuesday, she read 36% of the book. On Wednesday, she read 0.27 of the book. She finished the book on Thursday. What percent of the book did she read on Thursday?   _____

15. An airplane traveled from Boston to Las Vegas making a stop in St. Louis. The plane traveled 2410 miles altogether, which is 230% of the distance from Boston to St. Louis. Find the distance from Boston to St. Louis to the nearest mile.   _____

16. The first social studies test had 16 questions. The second test had 220% as many questions as the first test. Find the number of questions on the second test.   _____

Holt Mathematics

Name _____ Date _____ Class _____

Find each number to the nearest tenth.

1. 40% of what number is 18?

_____

2. 28 is 35% of what number?

_____

3. 21 is 60% of what number?

_____

4. 25% of what number is 19?

_____

5. 40% of what number is 22?

_____

6. 41 is 50% of what number?

_____

7. 50 is 15% of what number?

_____

8. 0.3% of what number is 24?

_____

9. 36 is 30% of what number?

_____

10. 26 is 75% of what number?

_____

11. 12.5% of what number is 14?

_____

12. 25% of what number is 28.25?

_____

13. 27 is $33\frac{1}{3}$% of what number?

_____

14. 54 is 150% of what number?

_____

15. There were 546 students at a school assembly. This was 65% of all students who attend Content Middle School. How many students attend Content Middle School?

_____

16. On his last test Greg answered 64 questions correctly. This was 80% of the questions. How many questions were on the test?

_____

17. The price of a jacket is $48. If the sales tax rate is 5.5%, what is the amount of tax? What is the total cost of the jacket?

_____

18. Carla has finished swimming 14 laps in swim practice. This is 70% of the total number of laps she must swim. How many more laps must Carla swim to complete her practice?

_____

Holt Mathematics

LESSON 6-5 Practice

Percent Increase and Decrease

Find each percent increase or decrease to the nearest percent.

1. from 16 to 20

2. from 30 to 24

3. from 15 to 30

_____

_____

_____

4. from 35 to 21

5. from 40 to 46

6. from 45 to 63

_____

_____

_____

7. from 18 to 26.1

8. from 24.5 to 21.56

9. from 90 to 72

_____

_____

_____

10. from 29 to 54

11. from 42 to 92.4

12. from 38 to 33

_____

_____

_____

13. from 64 to 36.4

14. from 78 to 136.5

15. from 89 to 32.9

_____

_____

_____

16. Mr. Havel bought a car for $2400 and sold it for $2700. What was the percent of profit for Mr. Havel in selling the car? _____

17. A computer store buys a computer program for $24 and sells it for $91.20. What is the percent of increase in the price? _____

18. A manufacturing company with 450 employees begins a new product line and must add 81 more employees. What is the percent of increase in the number of employees? _____

19. Richard earns $2700 a month. He received a 3% raise. What is Richard's new annual salary? _____

20. Marlis has 765 cards in her baseball card collection. She sells 153 of the cards. What is the percent of decrease in the number of cards in the collection? _____

Holt Mathematics

LESSON 6-6 Practice

Applications of Percents

Complete the table to find the amount of sales tax for each sale amount to the nearest cent.

1.

Sale amount	5% sales tax	8% sales tax	6.5% sales tax
$67.50			
$98.75			
$399.79			
$1250.00			

Complete the table to find the commission for each sale amount to the nearest cent.

2.

Sale amount	6% commision	9% commision	8.5% commission
$475.00			
$2450.00			
$12,500.00			
$98,900.00			

3. Alice earns a monthly salary of $315 plus a commission on her total sales. Last month her total sales were $9640, and she earned a total of $1182.60. What is her commission rate? _____

4. Phillipe works for a computer store that pays a 12% commission and no salary. What will Phillipe's weekly sales have to be for him to earn $360? _____

5. The purchase price of a book is $35.85. The sales tax rate is 6.5%. How much is the sales tax to the nearest cent? What is the total cost of the book?

_____

6. Who made more commission this month? How much did she make? Salesperson A made 11% of $67,530. Salesperson B made 8% of $85,740.

_____

7. Jon earned $38,000 last year. He paid $6,840 towards entertainment. What percent of his earnings did Jon pay in entertainment expenses? _____

8. The Cougars won 62% of their games. They won 93 games. How many games did they lose? _____

Holt Mathematics

LESSON **Practice**
6-7 *More Applications of Percents*

Find the missing value.

1. principal = $125

   rate = 4%

   time = 2 years

   interest = ?

   _____

2. principal = ?

   rate = 5%

   time = 4 years

   interest = $90

   _____

3. principal = $150

   rate = 6%

   time = ? years

   interest = $54

   _____

4. principal = $200

   rate = ?%

   time = 3 years

   interest = $30

   _____

5. principal = $550

   rate = ?%

   time = 3 years

   interest = $57.75

   _____

6. principal = ?

   rate = $3\frac{1}{4}$%

   time = 2 years

   interest = $63.05

   _____

7. Kwang deposits money in an account that earns 5% simple
   interest. He earned $546 in interest 2 years later. How much
   did he deposit?   _____

8. Simon opened a certificate of deposit with the money
   from his bonus check. The bank offered 4.5% interest for
   3 years of deposit. Simon calculated that he would earn
   $87.75 interest in that time. How much did Simon deposit
   to open the account?   _____

9. Douglas borrowed $1000 from Patricia. He agreed to
   repay her $1150 after 3 years. What was the interest
   rate of the loan?   _____

10. What is the interest paid for a loan of $800 at 5% annual
    interest for 9 months?   _____

Holt Mathematics

LESSON 7-1 Practice
Points, Lines, Planes, and Angles

Use the diagram to name each figure.

1. four points

_____

2. a line

_____

3. a plane

_____

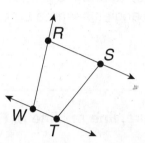

4. three segments

_____

5. four rays

_____

Use the diagram to name each figure.

6. a right angle

_____

7. two acute angles

_____

8. two obtuse angles

_____

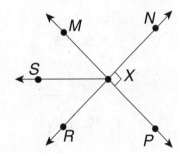

9. a pair of complementary angles

_____

_____

_____

10. three pairs of supplementary angles

_____

_____

_____

In the figure, ∠1 and ∠3 are vertical angles, and ∠2 and ∠4 are vertical angles.

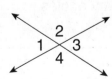

11. If m∠2 = 110°, find m∠4.

_____

12. If m∠1 = $n°$, find m∠3.

_____

Holt Mathematics

Name _____ Date _____ Class _____

1. Measure the angles formed by the
transversal and the parallel lines.
Which angles seem to be congruent?

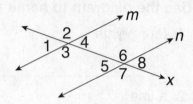

_____

_____

In the figure, line _m_ ∥ line _n_. Find the measure of each angle.

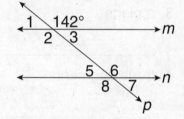

2. ∠1

3. ∠2

4. ∠5

_____   _____   _____

5. ∠6

6. ∠8

7. ∠7

_____   _____   _____

In the figure, line _a_ ∥ line _b_. Find the measure of each angle.

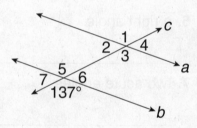

8. ∠2

9. ∠5

10. ∠6

_____   _____   _____

11. ∠7

12. ∠4

13. ∠3

_____   _____   _____

In the figure, line _r_ ∥ line _s_.

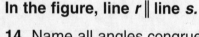

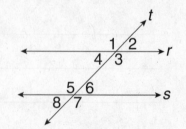

14. Name all angles congruent to ∠2.

_____

15. Name all angles congruent to ∠7.

_____

16. Name three pairs of supplementary angles.

_____

17. Which line is the transversal?

_____

Holt Mathematics

Name _____ Date _____ Class _____

1. Find $x°$ in the right triangle.

_____

2. Find $y°$ in the obtuse triangle.

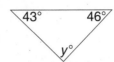

_____

3. Find $m°$ in the acute triangle.

_____

4. Find $n°$ in the obtuse triangle.

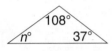

_____

5. Find $w°$ in the acute triangle.

_____

6. Find $t°$ in the right triangle.

_____

7. Find $t°$ in the scalene triangle.

_____

8. Find $x°$ in the isosceles triangle.

_____

9. Find $n°$ in the scalene triangle.

_____

10. Find $x°$ in the isosceles triangle.

_____

11. Find y in the equilateral triangle.

_____

12. Find r in the isoceles triangle.

_____

13. The second angle in a triangle is one third as large as the first. The third angle is two thirds as large as the first angle. Find the angle measures. Draw a possible picture of the triangle.

_____

Holt Mathematics

Name _____ Date _____ Class _____

Practice
Classifying Polygons

Find the sum of the angle measures in each figure.

1.

_____

2.

_____

3.

_____

4.

_____

5.

_____

6.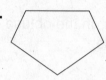

_____

Find the angle measures in each regular polygon.

7.

_____

8.

_____

9.

_____

10.

_____

11.

_____

12.

_____

Give all the names that apply to each figure.

13.

_____

_____

14.

_____

_____

15.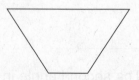

_____

_____

Holt Mathematics

Name _____ Date _____ Class _____

Determine if the slope of each line is positive, negative, 0, or undefined. Then find the slope of each line.

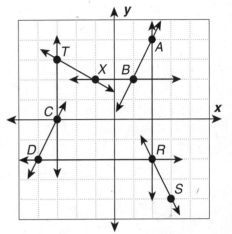

1. $\overleftrightarrow{AB}$

_____

2. $\overleftrightarrow{CD}$

_____

3. $\overleftrightarrow{RS}$

_____

4. $\overleftrightarrow{TC}$

_____

5. $\overleftrightarrow{DR}$

_____

6. $\overleftrightarrow{TX}$

_____

7. Which lines are parallel?

_____

8. Which lines are perpendicular?

_____

Graph the quadrilateral with the given vertices. Write all the names that apply to the quadrilateral.

9. $(-1, 1), (4, 1), (1, -3), (-4, -3)$

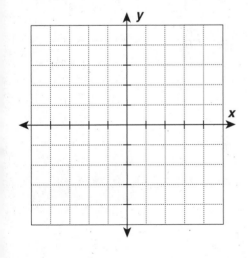

_____

Find the coordinates of the missing vertex.

10. rhombus *ABCD* with *A*(0, 4), *B*(4, 1), and *C*(0, –2)

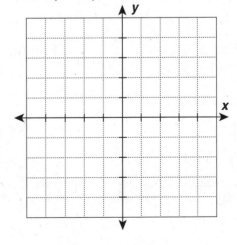

_____

51

Holt Mathematics

LESSON 7-6

Practice
Congruence

Write a congruence statement for each pair of polygons.

1.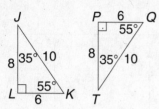

_____

_____

2.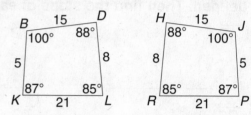

_____

_____

3.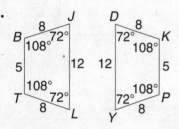

_____

_____

4.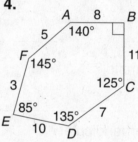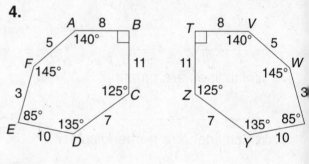

_____

_____

In the figure, triangle *PRT* ≅ triangle *FJH*.

5. Find *a*.

_____

6. Find *b*.

_____

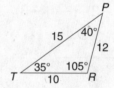 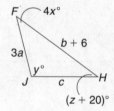

7. Find *c*.

_____

8. Find *x*.

_____

9. Find *y*.

_____

10. Find *z*.

_____

Holt Mathematics

Name _____ Date _____ Class _____

Identify each as a translation, rotation, reflection, or none of these.

1.

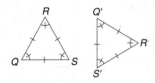

_____

2.

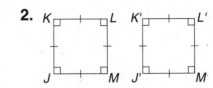

_____

Draw the image of the rectangle ABCD with vertices (−2, 1), (−1, 3), and (3, 3), (2, 1) after each transformation.

3. translation 3 units down

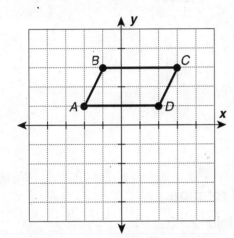

4. 180° rotation around (0, 0)

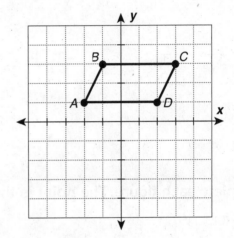

Triangle ABC has vertices A(−3, 1), B(2, 4), and C(3, 1). Find the coordinates of the image of each point after each transformation.

5. reflection across the x-axis, point B

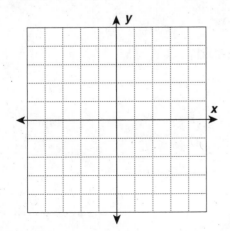

_____

6. translation 6 units down, point A

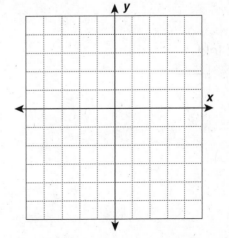

_____

Holt Mathematics

Name _____ Date _____ Class _____

LESSON **Practice**
7-8 *Symmetry*

Complete each figure. The dashed line is the line of symmetry.

1.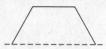

2.

3.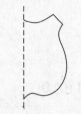

4.

5.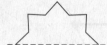

6.

Complete each figure. The point is the center of rotation.

7. 5-fold

8. 4-fold

9. 2-fold

10. 2-fold

Holt Mathematics

Practice

LESSON 7-9

Tessellations

1. Create a tessellation with quadrilateral *ABCD*.

2. Use rotations to create a variation of the tessellation in Exercise 1.

3. Create a tessellation with hexagon ABCDEF.

4. Use rotations to create a variation of the tessellation in Exercise 3.

Holt Mathematics

Name _____ Date _____ Class _____

Practice
Perimeter and Area of Rectangles and Parallelograms

Find the perimeter of each figure.

1.
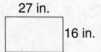
27 in.
16 in.

_____

2.
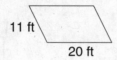
11 ft
20 ft

_____

3.
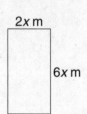
2x m
6x m

_____

Graph and find the area of each figure with the given vertices.

4. (−3, 4), (3, 4), (3, −4), (−3, −4)

5. (−1, 3), (2, 3), (−1, −4), (−4, −4)

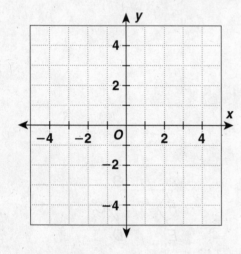

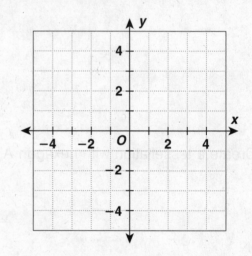

_____

_____

6. Sloppi and Sons Painting Co. charges its customers $1.50 per square foot. How much would Sloppi and Sons charge to paint the rooms of this house if the walls in each room are 9 ft high?

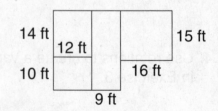
14 ft
12 ft
10 ft
9 ft
15 ft
16 ft

_____

Holt Mathematics

Name _____ Date _____ Class _____

Practice
Perimeter and Area of Triangles and Trapezoids

Find the perimeter of each figure.

1.

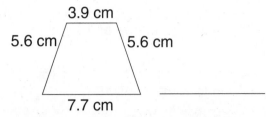

3.9 cm

5.6 cm   5.6 cm

7.7 cm

_____

2.

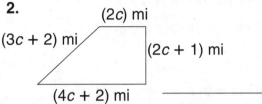

(2c) mi

(3c + 2) mi

(2c + 1) mi

(4c + 2) mi

_____

Find the missing measurement for each figure with the given perimeter.

3. triangle with
perimeter
54 units

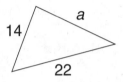

14   a

22

_____

4. trapezoid with
perimeter
34 units

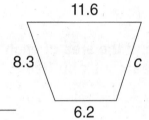

11.6

8.3   c

6.2

_____

Graph and find the area of each figure with the given vertices.

5. (−1, 3), (4, 3), (4, −4), (−4, −4)

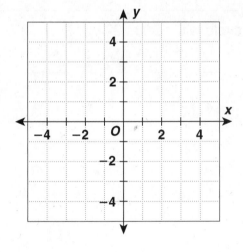

_____

6. (−1, 2), (−4, −2), (4, −2)

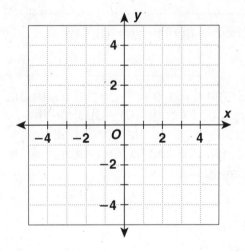

_____

7. The two shortest sides of a pennant shaped like a right triangle
measure 10 inches and 24 inches. Hank wants to put colored
tape around the edge of the pennant. How many inches of tape
does he need?

_____

Holt Mathematics

LESSON 8-3 Practice

Circles

Find the circumference of each circle, both in terms of π and to the nearest tenth. Use 3.14 for π.

1. circle with radius 10 in.

_____

2. circle with diameter 13 cm

_____

3. circle with diameter 18 m

_____

4. circle with radius 15 ft

_____

5. circle with radius 11.5 in.

_____

6. circle with diameter 16.4 cm

_____

Find the area of each circle, both in terms of π and to the nearest tenth. Use 3.14 for π.

7. circle with radius 9 in.

_____

8. circle with diameter 14 cm

_____

9. circle with radius 20 ft

_____

10. circle with diameter 17 m

_____

11. circle with diameter 15.4 m

_____

12. circle with radius 22 yd

_____

13. Graph a circle with center (0, 0) that passes through (0, −3). Find the area and circumference, both in terms of π and to the nearest tenth. Use 3.14 for π.

_____

_____

14. A wheel has a radius of 2 1\3 feet. About how far does it travel if it makes 60 complete revolutions? Use $\frac{22}{7}$ for π.

_____

Holt Mathematics

Name _____ Date _____ Class _____

1. Name the vertices, edges, and faces of the three-dimensional figure shown.

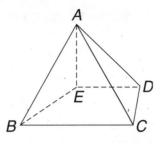

_____

edges: _____

faces: _____

2. Draw the figure that has the following top, front, and side views.

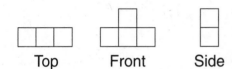

Top   Front   Side

3. Draw the front, top, and side views of the figure.

Name _____ Date _____ Class _____

LESSON **Practice**
8-5 *Volume of Prisms and Cylinders*

Find the volume of each figure to the nearest tenth. Use 3.14 for π.

1.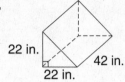
22 in.
22 in.
42 in.

_____

2. 6.5 cm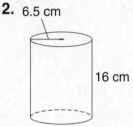
16 cm

_____

3.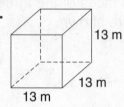
13 m
13 m
13 m

_____

4.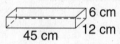
6 cm
12 cm
45 cm

_____

5.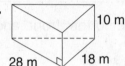
10 m
28 m   18 m

_____

6.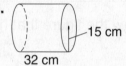
15 cm
32 cm

_____

7.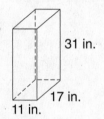
31 in.
17 in.
11 in.

_____

8.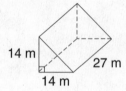
14 m
27 m
14 m

_____

9.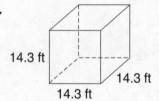
14.3 ft
14.3 ft
14.3 ft

_____

10. A cylinder has a radius of 6 ft and a height of 25 ft. Explain whether tripling the height will triple the volume of the cylinder.

_____

_____

11. Contemporary American building bricks are rectangular blocks with the standard dimensions of about 5.7 cm by 9.5 cm by 20.3 cm. What is the volume of a brick to the nearest tenth of a unit?

_____

12. Ian is making candles. His cylindrical mold is 8 in. tall and has a base with a diameter of 3 in. Find the volume of a finished candle to the nearest tenth of a unit.

_____

60
Holt Mathematics

Name _____ Date _____ Class _____

Practice

Volume of Pyramids and Cones

Find the volume of each figure to the nearest tenth. Use 3.14 for π.

1.
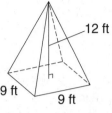
12 ft
9 ft
9 ft

_____

2.
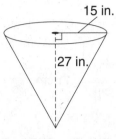
15 in.
27 in.

_____

3.
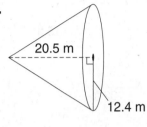
20.5 m
12.4 m

_____

4.
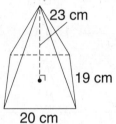
23 cm
19 cm
20 cm

_____

5.
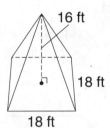
16 ft
18 ft
18 ft

_____

6.
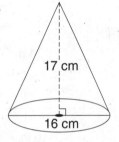
17 cm
16 cm

_____

7. The base of a regular pyramid has an area of 28 in². The height of the pyramid is 15 in. Find the volume.

_____

8. The radius of a cone is 19.4 cm and its height is 24 cm. Find the volume of the cone to the nearest tenth.

_____

9. Find the volume of a rectangular pyramid if the height is 13 m and the base sides are 12 m and 15 m.

_____

10. A funnel has a diameter of 9 in. and is 16 in. deep. Use a calculator to find the volume of the funnel to the nearest hundredth.

_____

11. A square pyramid has a height 18 cm and a base that measures 12 cm on each side. Explain whether tripling the height would triple the volume of the pyramid.

_____

_____

_____

Holt Mathematics

Name _____ Date _____ Class _____

Practice

Surface Area of Prisms and Cylinders

Find the surface area of each figure to the nearest tenth. Use 3.14 for π.

1.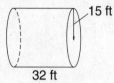

2.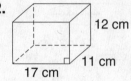

3.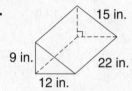

_____   _____   _____

4.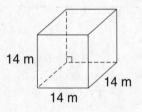

5.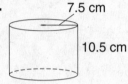

6.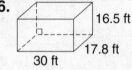

_____   _____   _____

7.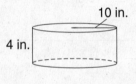

8.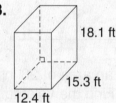

9.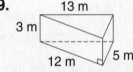

_____   _____   _____

10. Find the surface area to the nearest tenth of a rectangular prism with height 15 m and sides 14 m and 13 m.   _____

11. Find the surface area to the nearest tenth of a cylinder 61.7 ft tall that has a diameter of 38 ft.   _____

12. Henry wants to paint the ceiling and walls of his living room. One gallon of paint covers 450 ft^2. The room is 24 ft by 18 ft, and the walls are 9 ft high. How many full gallons of paint will Henry need to paint his living room?   _____

13. A rectangular prism is 18 in. by 16 in. by 10 in. Explain the effect, if any, tripling all the dimensions will have on the surface area of the figure.

_____

_____

Holt Mathematics

Name _____ Date _____ Class _____

Practice
Surface Area of Pyramids and Cones

**Find the surface area of each figure to the nearest tenth.
Use 3.14 for π.**

1.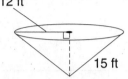

_____

2.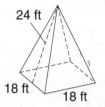

_____

3.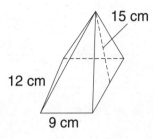

_____

4.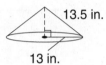

_____

5.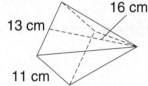

_____

6.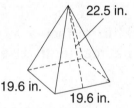

_____

7.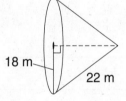

_____

8.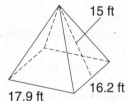

_____

9.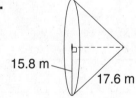

_____

10. Find the surface area of a regular square pyramid with a
slant height of 17 m and a base perimeter of 44 m.   _____

11. Find the length of the slant height of a square pyramid if
one side of the base is 15 ft and the surface area is 765 ft^2.   _____

12. Find the length of the slant height of a cone with a radius of
15 cm and a surface area of 1884 cm^2.   _____

13. A cone has a diameter of 12 ft and a slant height of 20 ft.
Explain whether tripling both dimensions would triple the
surface area.

_____

_____

_____

Holt Mathematics

Name _____ Date _____ Class _____

Practice

Spheres

Find the volume of each sphere, both in terms of π and to the nearest tenth. Use 3.14 for π.

1. $r = 9$ ft.   **2.** $r = 21$ m   **3.** $d = 30$ cm

_____   _____   _____

_____   _____   _____

4. $d = 24$ cm   **5.** $r = 15.4$ in.   **6.** $r = 16.01$ ft

_____   _____   _____

_____   _____   _____

Find the surface area of each sphere, both in terms of π and to the nearest tenth. Use 3.14 for π.

7.

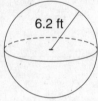

6.2 ft

8.

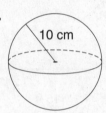

10 cm

9.

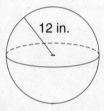

12 in.

_____   _____   _____

_____   _____   _____

10.

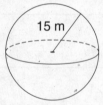

15 m

11.

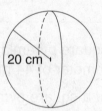

20 cm

12.

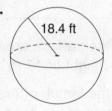

18.4 ft

_____   _____   _____

_____   _____   _____

13. In the sport of track and field, a field event is the shot put. This is a game in which a heavy ball or shot is thrown or put for distance. The shot itself comes in various sizes, weights and composition. Find the volume and surface area of a shot with diameter 5.5 cm both in terms of π and to the nearest tenth.

_____

_____

Holt Mathematics

Name _____ Date _____ Class _____

Practice

Scaling Three-Dimensional Figures

A 10 in. cube is built from small cubes, each 2 in. on a side.
Compare the following values.

1. The side lengths of the two cubes

   _____

   _____

2. The surface area of the two cubes

   _____

3. The volumes of the two cubes

   _____

A 9 cm cube is built from small cubes, each 3 cm on a side.
Compare the following values.

4. The side lengths of the two cubes

   _____

   _____

5. The surface area of the two cubes

   _____

6. The volumes of the two cubes

   _____

7. The dimensions of a warehouse are 120 ft long, 180 ft wide, and
   60 ft high. The scale model used to build the warehouse is 20
   in. long. Find the width and height of the model of the
   warehouse.

   _____

8. It takes a machine 40 seconds to fill a cubic box with sides
   measuring 10 in. How long will it take the same machine to fill a
   cubic box with sides measuring 15 in.?

   _____

Holt Mathematics

LESSON 9-1 Practice

Samples and Surveys

Identify the sampling method used.

1. People in the security line at the airport are asked to step out of the line for a more detailed search. The people pulled out of the line have not necessarily done anything wrong, and they are not chosen according to any particular rule.

   _____

2. At the 1-mile marker of a marathon, a timekeeper shouts out the time elapsed to every 10th runner that passes by. A statistician records the times shouted.

   _____

3. A geologist visits 10 randomly-selected lakes in the region and collects soil samples in randomly-selected areas along each shoreline.

   _____

Identify the population and sample. Give a reason the sample could be biased.

4. At a convention of science teachers, various attendees are asked to name their favorite subject in high school.

   population _____

   sample _____

   possible bias _____

5. Donors participating in a blood drive are given a small amount of money for their blood donation. Before they can give blood, each person is surveyed to find out if they are eligible to give blood.

   population _____

   sample _____

   possible bias _____

6. Interviewers at the mall are surveying girls with red hair to find out if a correlation exists between personality and red hair.

   population _____

   sample _____

   possible bias _____

Holt Mathematics

Name _____ Date _____ Class _____

LESSON 9-2

Practice

Organizing Data

1. Use a line plot to organize the data of the distances students travel to school.

Distances Students Travel to School (mi)

2	8	6	10	5	4	6	8	3	2
11	5	1	3	6	5	7	5	2	4

List the data values in the stem-and-leaf plot.

2.

```
2 | 0  1  5  7
3 | 2  2  9
4 | 5  6  7  9
5 | 1  3        Key: 5 | 1 = 51
```

_____

_____

3. Use the given data to make a back-to-back stem-and-leaf plot.

NBA Midwest Division 2000–2001 Final Standings

NBA Team	Wins	Losses	NBA Team	Wins	Losses
San Antonio Spurs	58	24	Houston Rockets	45	37
Utah Jazz	53	29	Denver Nuggets	40	42
Dallas Mavericks	53	29	Vancouver Grizzlies	23	59
Minnesota Timberwolves	47	35			

Wins		Losses

Key:

4. Make a Venn diagram to show how many girls in an eighth-grade class belonged to both a team and a club.

Team	yes	no	yes	no	yes	yes	yes	no	no	yes	no	no
Club	yes	yes	no	yes	yes	no	yes	yes	yes	no	no	yes

67

Holt Mathematics

Name _____ Date _____ Class _____

Practice

9-3 *Measures of Central Tendency*

Find the mean, median, mode, and range of each data set.

1. 7, 7, 4, 9, 6, 4, 5, 8, 4

mean: _____

median: _____

mode: _____

range: _____

2. 1.2, 5.8, 3.7, 9.7, 5.5, 0.3, 8.1

mean: _____

median: _____

mode: _____

range: _____

3. 31, 28, 31, 30, 31, 30,
31, 31, 30, 31, 30, 31

mean: _____

median: _____

mode: _____

range: _____

4. 65, 46, 78, 3, 87,
12, 99, 38, 71, 38

mean: _____

median: _____

mode: _____

range: _____

Determine and find the most appropriate measure of central tendency or range for each situation. Refer to the table at the right for Exercises 5–7.

5. Which measure best describes the middle of the data?

_____

6. Which earthquake magnitude occurred most frequently?

_____

7. How spread out are the data?

_____

Some Major Earthquakes in United States History

Year	Location	Magnitude
1812	Missouri	7.9
1872	California	7.8
1906	California	7.7
1957	Alaska	8.8
1964	Alaska	9.2
1965	Alaska	8.7
1983	Idaho	7.3
1986	Alaska	8.0
1987	Alaska	7.9
1992	California	7.6

8. Nicole purchased gasoline 8 times in the last two months. The prices that she paid per gallon each time were $2.19, $2.14, $2.28, $2.09, $2.01, $1.99, $2.19, and $2.39. Which measure makes the prices appear lowest?

_____

Holt Mathematics

Name _____ Date _____ Class _____

Find the first and third quartiles for each data set.

1. 37, 48, 56, 35, 53, 41, 50

first quartile: _____

third quartile: _____

2. 18, 20, 34, 33, 16, 44, 42, 27

first quartile: _____

third quartile: _____

Use the given data to make a box-and-whisker plot.

3. 55, 46, 70, 36, 43, 45, 52, 61

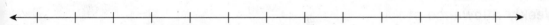

4. 23, 34, 31, 16, 38, 42, 45, 30, 28, 25, 19, 32, 53

Use the box-and-whisker plots to compare the data sets.

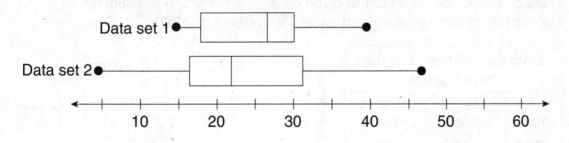

5. Compare the medians and ranges.

_____

_____

6. Compare the ranges of the middle half of the data for each set.

_____

_____

Holt Mathematics

Name _____ Date _____ Class _____

Displaying Data

1. Make a double-bar graph.

Daily Hours Worked	6	7	8	9	10	11	12
Crew A	4	3	6	1	3	1	2
Crew B	5	5	4	3	2	0	1

Daily Hours Worked by Two Crews

Frequency

Hours Worked

2. Use the data to make a histogram with intervals of 5.

Weekly Allowance of 20 Students			
$5	$15	$2	$10
$12	$12	$10	$15
$10	$5	$6	$4
$8	$7	$20	$7
$5	$4	$5	$9

Number of Students

Allowance (dollars)

3. Make a double-line graph of the given data. Use the graph to estimate the number of radio stations and cable TV systems in 2002.

Commercial Media in the United States		
Year	Radio Stations	Cable TV Systems
1997	10,207	10,950
1999	10,444	10,700
2001	10,516	9,924
2003	10,605	9,339

Number of Enterprises

U.S. Commercial Media

Year

Holt Mathematics

Name _____ Date _____ Class _____

Practice
Misleading Graphs and Statistics

Explain why each graph is misleading.

1.
On the Road
Number of Trucks that Travel City Roads

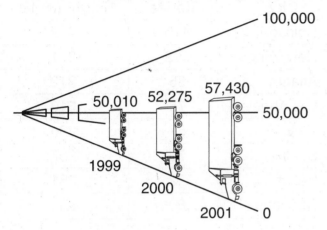

_____
_____
_____
_____
_____
_____
_____
_____

2.
Federal Minimun Wage Rates Since 1980

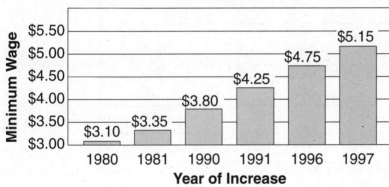

_____

_____

_____

Explain why the statistic is misleading.

3. A chewing gum company advertises that the flavor of its new
   chewing gum lasts for an average of 55 minutes based on the
   following durations reported by customers: 12 min, 33 min,
   5 min, 200 min, and 25 min.

_____

_____

_____

Holt Mathematics

Name _____ Date _____ Class _____

Practice
Scatter Plots

1. Use the given data to make a scatter plot.

Tall Buildings in U.S. Cities

Building	City	Stories	Height (meters)
Sears Tower	Chicago	110	442
Empire State Building	New York	102	381
Bank of America Plaza	Atlanta	55	312
Library Tower	Los Angeles	75	310
Key Tower	Cleveland	57	290
Columbia Seafirst Center	Seattle	76	287
NationsBank Plaza	Dallas	72	281
NationsBank Corporate Center	Charlotte	60	265

Tall Buildings in U.S. Cities

Do the data sets have a positive, a negative, or no correlation?

2. The temperature outside and the number of ice cream cones sold

_____

3. The amount of time spent in the bathtub and the temperature of the bath water

_____

4. Use the data to predict the percent of Americans owning a home in 1955.

Percent of Americans Owning Homes

Year	1950	1960	1970	1980	1990
Percent	55.0%	61.9%	62.9%	64.4%	64.2%

According to the data, about _____% of Americans owned a home in 1955.

Holt Mathematics

LESSON
9-8

Practice

9-8 *Choosing the Best Representation of Data*

1. Which graph is a better display of the number of students in a class who chose math as their favorite subject?

Students' Favorite Subjects

10%

40%

30%

20%

☐ Math
■ Social Studies
☐ English
■ Reading

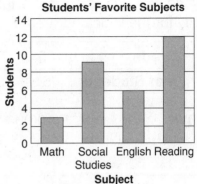

_____

_____

2. Which graph is a better display of the change in the number of cell telephone subscribers?

U.S. Cellular Telephone Subscribers
(millions)

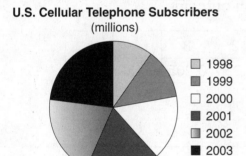

☐ 1998
■ 1999
☐ 2000
■ 2001
■ 2002
■ 2003

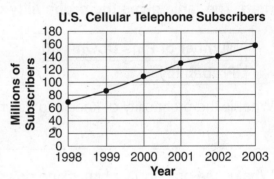

_____

_____

3. The table shows the heights of players on a school basketball team. Choose an appropriate data display and draw the graph.

Heights of Basketball Players (in.)			
70	64	68	71
61	68	65	73

Holt Mathematics

LESSON **Practice**
10-1 *Probability*

These are the results of the last math test. The teacher determines that anyone with a grade of more than 70 passed the test. Give the probability for the indicated grade.

Grade	65	70	80	90	100
# of Students	5	3	12	10	2

1. $P(70)$ **2.** $P(100)$ **3.** $P(80)$ **4.** $P(\text{passing})$

_____   _____   _____   _____

5. $P(\text{grade} > 80)$ **6.** $P(60)$ **7.** $P(\text{failing})$ **8.** $P(\text{grade} \leq 80)$

_____   _____   _____   _____

A bowling game consists of rolling a ball and knocking up to 5 pins down. The number of pins knocked down are then counted. The table gives the probability of each outcome.

Number of Pins Down	0	1	2	3	4	5
Probability	0.175	0.189	0.264	0.205	0.132	0.035

9. What is the probability of knocking down all 5 pins?

_____

10. What is the probability of knocking down no pins?

_____

11. What is the probability of knocking down at most 2 pins?

_____

12. What is the probability of knocking down at least 2 pins?

_____

13. What is the probability of knocking down more than 3 pins?

_____

Holt Mathematics

Name _____ Date _____ Class _____

1. A number cube was thrown 150 times. The results are shown in the table below. Estimate the probability for each outcome.

Outcome	1	2	3	4	5	6
Frequency	33	21	15	36	27	18
Probability						

A movie theater sells popcorn in small, medium, large and jumbo sizes. The customers of the first show purchase 4 small, 20 medium, 40 large, and 16 jumbo containers of popcorn. Estimate the probability of the purchase of each of the different size containers of popcorn.

2. P(small container)

3. P(medium container)

_____

_____

4. P(large container)

5. P(jumbo container)

_____

_____

Janessa polled 154 students about their favorite winter sport.

Outcome	Frequency
Skiing	46
Sledding	21
Snowboarding	64
Ice Skating	14
Other	9

6. Use the table to compare the probability that a student chose snowboarding to the probability that a student chose skiing.

_____

7. Use the table to compare the probability that a student chose ice skating to the probability that a student chose sledding.

_____

8. The class president made 75 copies of the flyer advertising the school play. It was found that 8 of the copies were defective. Estimate the probability that a flyer will be printed properly. _____

Holt Mathematics

Name _____ Date _____ Class _____

Use the table of random numbers for the problems below.

8125	4764	7693	3675	1642	7988	7048	9135	3138	3256
9566	4413	7215	7992	4320	7438	3805	5473	8847	2397
7336	5393	8623	8570	5095	5685	6695	3570	3605	4656
6470	6065	8239	2953	5942	6496	8899	0701	5368	2106
5210	2570	8137	3587	3578	6657	6636	7188	5717	1770
4329	4110	2655	8258	9928	3873	5609	3695	7091	0368
5315	2654	0484	4601	4336	6624	5403	5870	8545	3905
2361	9097	3753	2498	0544	0923	6099	1737	4025	1221
2677	7741	5342	9844	3722	5120	8742	1382	2842	7386
3292	5084	1130	2747	0664	9718	6072	9432	7008	2024

Mr. Domino gave the same math test to all three of his math
classes. In the first two classes, 80% of the students passed the
test. If the third class has 20 students, estimate the number of
students who will pass the test.

1. Using the first row as the first trial, count the successful
outcomes and name the unsuccessful outcomes.

_____

2. Count and name the successful outcomes in the second row as
the second trial.

_____

**Determine the successful outcomes in the remaining rows of
the random number table.**

3. third row   **4.** fourth row   **5.** fifth row   **6.** sixth row

_____   _____   _____   _____

7. seventh row   **8.** eighth row   **9.** ninth row   **10.** tenth row

_____   _____   _____   _____

11. Based on the simulation, estimate the probability that 80% of
the class will pass the math test. _____

Holt Mathematics

Name _____ Date _____ Class _____

An experiment consists of rolling one fair number cube.
Find the probability of each event.

1. $P(3)$

2. $P(7)$

_____

_____

3. $P(1 \text{ or } 4)$

4. $P(\text{not } 5)$

_____

_____

5. $P(< 5)$

6. $P(> 4)$

_____

_____

7. $P(2 \text{ or odd})$

8. $P(\leq 3)$

_____

_____

An experiment consists of rolling two fair number cubes.
Find the probability of each event.

9. $P(\text{total shown} = 3)$

10. $P(\text{total shown} = 7)$

11. $P(\text{total shown} = 9)$

_____

_____

_____

12. $P(\text{total shown} = 2)$

13. $P(\text{total shown} = 4)$

14. $P(\text{total shown} = 13)$

_____

_____

_____

15. $P(\text{total shown} > 8)$

16. $P(\text{total shown} \leq 12)$

17. $P(\text{total shown} < 7)$

_____

_____

_____

18. A bag contains 9 pennies, 8 nickels, and 5 dimes. How many
quarters should be added to the bag so the probability of
drawing a dime is $\frac{1}{6}$? _____

19. In a game two fair number cubes are rolled. To make the
first move, you need to roll a total of 6, 7, or 8. What is the
probability that you will be able to make the first move? _____

Holt Mathematics

Name _____ Date _____ Class _____

Practice
10-5 *Independent and Dependent Events*

Determine if the events are dependent or independent.

1. choosing a tie and shirt from the closet   _____

2. choosing a month and tossing a coin   _____

3. rolling two fair number cubes once, then rolling them
   again if you received the same number on both number
   cubes on the first roll   _____

An experiment consists of rolling a fair number cube and tossing a fair coin.

4. Find the probability of getting a 5 on the number cube and tails
   on the dime.   _____

5. Find the probability of getting an even number on the number
   cube and heads on the dime.   _____

6. Find the probability of getting a 2 or 3 on the number cube and
   heads on the dime.   _____

A box contains 3 red marbles, 6 blue marbles, and 1 white marble. The marbles are selected at random, one at a time, and are not replaced. Find the probability.

7. *P*(blue and red)   8. *P*(white and blue)   9. *P*(red and white)

_____   _____   _____

10. *P*(red and white and   11. *P*(red and red and   12. *P*(red and blue and
    blue)   blue)   blue)

_____   _____   _____

13. *P*(red and red and   14. *P*(white and blue   15. *P*(white and red
    red)   and blue)   and white)

_____   _____   _____

          Holt Mathematics

LESSON 10-6 Practice

Making Decisions and Predictions

A sports store sells water bottles in different colors. The table shows the colors of the last 200 water bottles sold. The manager plans to order 1800 new water bottles.

Water Bottles Sold

Color	Number
Red	30
Blue	50
Green	25
Yellow	10
Purple	10
Clear	75

1. How many red water bottles should the manager order? _____

2. How many green water bottles should the manager order? _____

3. How many clear water bottles should the manager order? _____

4. If the carnival spinner lands on 10, the player gets a large stuffed animal. Suppose the spinner is spun 30 times. Predict how many large stuffed animals will be given away. _____

Decide whether the game is fair.

5. Roll two fair number cubes labeled 1–6. Player A wins if both numbers are the same. Player B wins if both numbers are different.

_____

6. Roll two fair number cubes labeled 1–6. Add the numbers. Player A wins if the sum is 5 or less. Player B wins if the sum is 9 or more.

_____

7. Toss three fair coins. Player A wins if exactly one tail lands up. Otherwise, Player B wins.

Holt Mathematics

LESSON **Practice**
10-7 *Odds*

**A bag contains 9 red marbles, 5 green marbles, and
6 purple marbles.**

1. Find *P*(red marble)   **2.** Find *P*(green marble)   **3.** Find *P*(purple marble)

_____   _____   _____

4. Find the odds in favor of choosing a red marble.

_____

5. Find the odds against choosing a red marble.

_____

6. Find the odds in favor of choosing a green marble.

_____

7. Find the odds against choosing a green marble.

_____

8. Find the odds in favor of choosing a purple marble.

_____

9. Find the odds against choosing a purple marble.

_____

10. Find the odds in favor of not choosing a green marble.

_____

11. Find the odds in favor of choosing a red or purple marble.

_____

12. If the probability of Helena winning the contest is $\frac{2}{5}$, what
are the odds in favor of Helena winning the contest?

_____

13. The odds in favor of the Bruins winning the Stanley Cup
are 5 to 4. What is the probability that the Bruins will win
the Stanley Cup?

_____

                                       Holt Mathematics

Name _____ Date _____ Class _____

Practice
Counting Principles

**Employee identification codes at a company contain 2 letters
followed by 2 numbers. All codes are equally likely.**

1. Find the number of possible
   identification codes.

2. Find the probability of being assigned
   the code MT49.

_____

3. Find the probability that an ID code
   of the company does not contain the
   letter *A* as the second letter of the
   code.

4. Find the probability that an ID code
   of the company does not contain the
   number 2.

_____

5. Mrs. Sharpe is planning her dinners for next week. The choices
   for the entree are roast beef, turkey, or pork. The choices of
   carbohydrates are mashed potatoes, baked potatoes, or noodles.
   The vegetable choices are broccoli, spinach, or carrots. Make a
   tree diagram indicating the possible outcomes for each entree.

6. How many different meals could Mrs. Sharpe prepare? _____

Find the probability for each of the following.

7. *P*(dinner with baked potato)

8. *P*(dinner with noodles and carrots)

_____

9. Mitch bought 2 sports magazines, 3 guitar magazines, and
   3 news magazines. How many choices of magazines does
   he have to read?

_____

Holt Mathematics

LESSON 10-9 Practice
Permutations and Combinations

Evaluate each expression.

1. 10!

2. 13!

3. 11! − 8!

_____   _____   _____

4. 12! − 9!

5. $\dfrac{15!}{8!}$

6. $\dfrac{18!}{12!}$

_____   _____   _____

7. $\dfrac{13!}{(17-12)!}$

8. $\dfrac{19!}{(15-2)!}$

9. $\dfrac{15!}{(18-10)!}$

_____   _____   _____

10. Signaling is a means of communication through signals or objects. During the time of the American Revolution, the colonists used combinations of a barrel, basket, and a flag placed in different positions atop a post. How many different signals could be sent by using 3 flags, one above the other on a pole, if 8 different flags were available?

_____

11. From a class of 25 students, how many different ways can 4 students be selected to serve in a mock trial as the judge, defending attorney, prosecuting attorney, and the defendant?

_____

12. How many different 4 people committees can be formed from a group of 15 people?

_____

13. The girls' basketball team has 12 players. If the coach chooses 5 girls to play at a time, how many different teams can be formed?

_____

14. A photographer has 50 pictures to be placed in an album. How many combinations will the photographer have to choose from if there will be 6 pictures placed on the first page?

_____

Holt Mathematics

Practice
11-1 *Simplifying Algebraic Expressions*

Combine like terms.

1. $8a - 5a$

2. $12g + 7g$

3. $4a + 7a + 6$

_____   _____   _____

4. $6x + 3y + 5x$

5. $10k - 3k + 5h$

6. $3p - 7q + 14p$

_____   _____   _____

7. $3k + 7k + 5k$

8. $5c + 12d - 6$

9. $13 + 4b + 6b - 5$

_____   _____   _____

10. $4f + 6 + 7f - 2$

11. $x + y + 3x + 7y$

12. $9n + 13 - 8n - 6$

_____   _____   _____

Simplify.

13. $4(x + 3) - 5$

14. $6(7 + x) + 5x$

15. $3(5 + 3x) - 4x$

_____   _____   _____

Solve.

16. $6y + 2y = 16$

17. $14b - 9b = 35$

18. $3q + 9q = 48$

_____   _____   _____

19. Gregg has q quarters and p pennies. His brother has 4 times
as many quarters and 8 times as many pennies as Gregg has.
Write the sum of the number of coins they have, and then
combine like terms.

_____

20. If Gregg has 6 quarters and 15 pennies, how many total coins
do Gregg and his brother have?

_____

Holt Mathematics

Name _____ Date _____ Class _____

Solve.

1. $2x + 5x + 4 = 25$

_____

2. $9 + 3y - 2y = 14$

_____

3. $16 = 4w + 2w - 2$

_____

4. $26 = 3b - 2 - 7b$

_____

5. $31 + 4t - t = 40$

_____

6. $14 - 2x + 4x = 20$

_____

7. $\dfrac{5m}{8} - \dfrac{6}{8} + \dfrac{3m}{8} = \dfrac{2}{8}$

_____

8. $-4\dfrac{2}{3} = \dfrac{2n}{3} + \dfrac{1}{3} + \dfrac{n}{3}$

_____

9. $7a + 16 - 3a = -4$

_____

10. $\dfrac{x}{2} + 1 + \dfrac{3x}{4} = -9$

_____

11. $7m + 3 - 4m = -9$

_____

12. $\dfrac{2x}{5} + 3 - \dfrac{4x}{5} = \dfrac{1}{5}$

_____

13. $\dfrac{7k}{8} - \dfrac{3}{4} - \dfrac{5k}{16} = \dfrac{3}{8}$

_____

14. $6y + 9 - 4y = -3$

_____

15. $\dfrac{5a}{6} - \dfrac{7}{12} + \dfrac{3a}{4} = -2\dfrac{1}{6}$

_____

16. The measure of an angle is 28° greater than its complement.
Find the measure of each angle.

_____

17. The measure of an angle is 21° more than twice its supplement.
Find the measure of each angle.

_____

18. The perimeter of the triangle is 126 units.
Find the measure of each side.

_____

_____

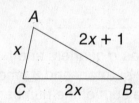

19. The base angles of an isosceles triangle
are congruent. If the measure of each of
the base
angles is twice the measure of the third
angle, find the measure of all three
angles.

_____

Holt Mathematics

Name _____ Date _____ Class _____

Solving Equations with Variables on Both Sides

Solve.

1. $7x - 11 = -19 + 3x$

2. $11a + 9 = 4a + 30$

3. $4t + 14 = \frac{6t}{5} + 7$

_____

_____

_____

4. $19c + 31 = 26c - 74$

5. $\frac{3y}{8} - 9 = 13 + \frac{y}{8}$

6. $\frac{3k}{5} + 44 = \frac{12k}{25} + 8$

_____

_____

_____

7. $10a - 37 = 6a + 51$

8. $5w + 9.9 = 4.8 + 8w$

9. $15 - x = 2(x + 3)$

_____

_____

_____

10. $15y + 14 = 2(5y + 6)$

11. $14 - \frac{w}{8} = \frac{3w}{4} - 21$

12. $\frac{1}{2}(6x - 4) = 4x - 9$

_____

_____

_____

13. $4(3d - 2) = 8d - 5$

14. $\frac{y}{3} + 11 = \frac{y}{2} - 3$

15. $\frac{2x - 9}{3} = 8 - 3x$

_____

_____

_____

16. Forty-eight decreased by a number is the same as
the difference of four times the number and seven.
Find the number.   _____

17. The square and the equilateral
triangle at the right have the same
perimeter. Find the length of the
sides of the triangle.

 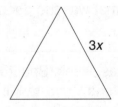

$x + 5$ $3x$

_____

Holt Mathematics

Name _____ Date _____ Class _____

Solve and graph.

1. $\frac{m}{-5} \le 4$

_____

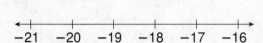

2. $-16 < -8n$

_____

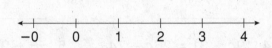

3. $7p \ge 49$

_____

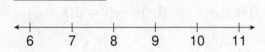

4. $10 > \frac{q}{2}$

_____

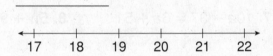

5. $-\frac{r}{3} \le 15$

_____

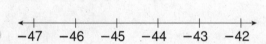

6. $22 > -2s$

_____

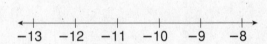

7. $-6t < -24$

_____

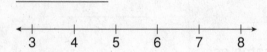

8. $\frac{v}{20} \ge 2$

_____

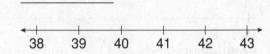

9. On a snorkeling trip, Antonia dove at least 7 times as deep as Lucy did. If Antonia dove 35 feet below the ocean's surface, what was the deepest that Lucy dove?

_____

10. Last week, Saul ran more than one-fifth the distance that his friend Omar ran. If Saul ran 14 miles last week, how far did Omar run?

_____

Holt Mathematics

Name _____ Date _____ Class _____

11-5 Solving Two-Step Inequalities

Solve and graph.

1. $4x - 2 < 26$

_____

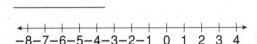

2. $6 - \frac{1}{5}y \leq 7$

_____

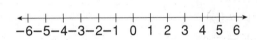

3. $2x + 27 \geq 15$

_____

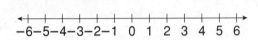

4. $10x > 14x + 8$

_____

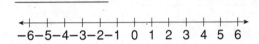

5. $7 - 4w \leq 19$

_____

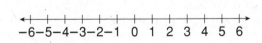

6. $\frac{k}{5} + \frac{3}{20} < \frac{3}{10}$

_____

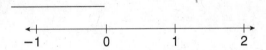

7. $4.8 - 9.6x \leq 14.4$

_____

8. $\frac{2}{9} + \frac{y}{3} > \frac{1}{3}$

_____

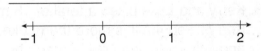

9. One-third of a number, decreased by thirty-six, is at most twenty-two. Find the number.

_____

10. Jack wants to run at least 275 miles before the baseball season begins. He has already run 25 miles. He plans to run 2.5 miles each day. At this rate, what is the fewest number of days he will need to reach his goal?

_____

Holt Mathematics

LESSON 11-6 Practice
Systems of Equations

Solve each system of equations.

1. $y = 2x - 4$
   $y = x - 1$

   _____

2. $y = -x + 10$
   $y = x + 2$

   _____

3. $y = 2x - 1$
   $y = -3x - 6$

   _____

4. $y = 2x$
   $y = 12 - x$

   _____

5. $y = 2x - 3$
   $y = 2x + 1$

   _____

6. $y = 3x - 1$
   $y = x + 1$

   _____

7. $x + y = 0$
   $5x + 2y = -3$

   _____

8. $2x - 3y = 0$
   $2x + y = 8$

   _____

9. $2x + 3y = 6$
   $4x + 6y = 12$

   _____

10. $6x - y = -14$
    $2x - 3y = 6$

    _____

11. The sum of two numbers is 24. The second number is 6 less
    than the first. Write a system of equations and solve it
    find the number.

    _____

15. Kerry and Luke biked a total of 18 miles in one weekend.
    Kerry biked 4 miles more than Luke. Write a system of equations
    and solve it to find how far each boy biked.

    _____

    _____

Holt Mathematics

Practice
Graphing Linear Equations

Graph each equation and tell whether it is linear.

1. $y = -2x - 5$

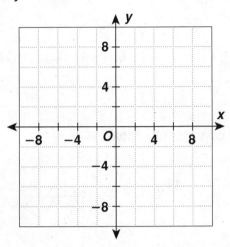

2. $y = -x^2 + 1$

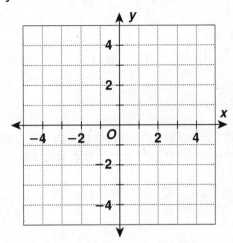

3. $y = x^2 - 7$

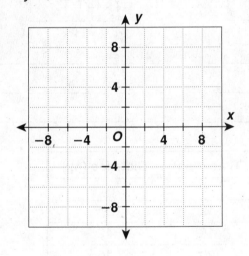

4. $y = \frac{1}{2}x - 1$

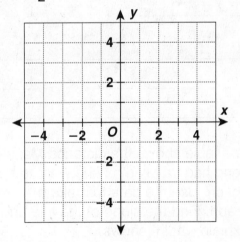

5. A real estate agent commission may be based on the equation $C = 0.06s + 450$, where s represents the total sales. If the agent sells a property for $125,000, what is the commission earned by the agent? Graph the equation and tell whether it is linear.

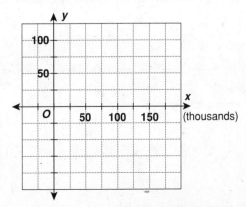

Holt Mathematics

Name _____ Date _____ Class _____

Find the slope of the line that passes through each pair of points.

1. (−2, −8), (1, 4)   **2.** (−2, 0), (0, 4),   **3.** (0, 4), (4, 4)   **4.** (3, −6), (2, −4)

_____   _____   _____   _____

5. (−3, 4), (3, −4)   **6.** (3, 0), (0, −6),   **7.** (3, 2), (3, −2)   **8.** (−4, 4), (3, −1)

_____   _____   _____   _____

Determine whether each graph shows a constant or variable rate of change. Explain your reasoning.

9.
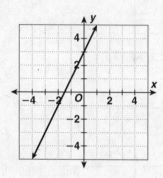

10.
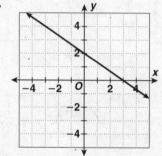

11.
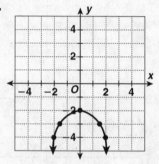

_____   _____   _____

_____   _____   _____

_____

12. The table shows the distance Ms. Long had traveled as she went to the beach. Use the data to make a graph. Find the slope of the line and explain what it shows.

Time (min)	Distance (mi)
8	6
12	9
16	12
20	15

_____

_____

_____

_____

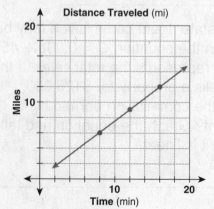

Distance Traveled (mi)

Name _____ Date _____ Class _____

Find the *x*-intercept and *y*-intercept of each line.
Use the intercepts to graph the equation.

1. $x - y = -3$

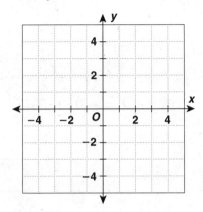

_____

_____

2. $2x + 3y = 12$

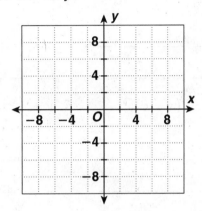

_____

_____

Write each equation in slope-intercept form, and then find
the slope and *y*-intercept.

3. $3x + y = 0$

_____

_____

4. $2x - y = -15$

_____

_____

5. $x - 5y = 10$

_____

_____

Write the equation of the line that passes through each pair of
points in slope-intercept form.

6. $(3, 4), (4, 6)$

_____

7. $(-1, -1), (2, -10)$

_____

8. $(6, 5), (-9, -20)$

_____

9. A pizzeria charges $8 for a large
cheese pizza, plus $2 for each topping.
The total cost for a large pizza is given
by the equation $C = 2t + 8$, where t is
the number of toppings. Identify the
slope and *y*-intercept, and use them
to graph the equation for *t* between 0
and 5 toppings.

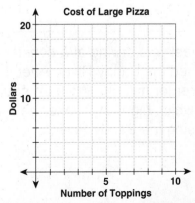

_____

Holt Mathematics

Practice

Point-Slope Form

Use the point-slope form of each equation to identify a point the line passes through and the slope of the line.

1. $y - 2 = 4(x - 1)$

2. $y + 1 = 2(x - 3)$

3. $y - 4 = -3(x + 1)$

_____

_____

4. $y + 5 = -2(x + 6)$

5. $y + 4 = -9(x + 3)$

6. $y - 7 = -7(x - 7)$

_____

_____

7. $y - 10 = 6(x - 8)$

8. $y + 12 = 2.5(x + 4)$

9. $y + 8 = \frac{1}{2}(x - 3)$

_____

_____

Write the point-slope form of the equation with the given slope that passes through the indicated point.

10. the line with slope -1 passing through $(2, 5)$

11. the line with slope 2 passing through $(-1, 4)$

_____

_____

12. the line with slope 4 passing through $(-3, -2)$

13. the line with slope 3 passing through $(7, -6)$

_____

_____

14. the line with slope -3 passing through $(-6, 4)$

15. the line with slope -2 passing through $(5, 1)$

_____

_____

16. Michael was driving at a constant speed of 60 mph when he crossed the Sandy River. After 1 hour, he passed a highway marker for mile 84. Write an equation in point-slope form, and find which highway marker he will pass 90 minutes after crossing the Sandy River.

_____

Holt Mathematics

Name _____ Date _____ Class _____

Practice
12-5 *Direct Variation*

Make a graph to determine whether the data sets show direct variation.

1.

x	y
6	9
4	6
0	0
−2	−3
−8	−12

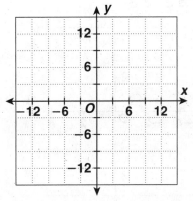

_____

2. Write the equation of direct variation for Exercise 1.

_____

Find each equation of direct variation, given that y varies with x.

3. *y* is 32 when *x* is 4

4. *y* is −10 when *x* is −20

5. *y* is 63 when *x* is −7

6. *y* is 40 when *x* is 50

7. *y* is 87.5 when *x* is 25

8. *y* is 90 when *x* is 270

9. The table shows the length and width of various U.S. flags. Determine whether there is direct variation between the two data sets. If so, find the equation of direct variation.

Length (ft)	2.85	5.7	7.6	9.88	11.4
Width (ft)	1.5	3	4	5.2	6

_____

_____

_____

Holt Mathematics

LESSON 12-6

Practice

Graphing Inequalities in Two Variables

Graph each inequality.

1. $y \geq 2x + 3$

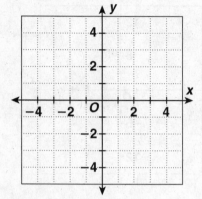

2. $y - 4x \leq 1$

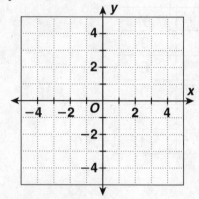

3. $2(3x - y) > 6$

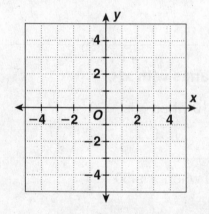

4. $y \geq \frac{3}{4}x - 1$

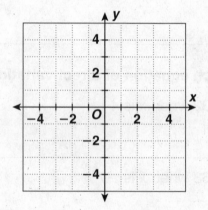

5. a. A theater club hopes to raise at least $550 on the opening night of its new show. Student tickets for the show cost $2.75, and adult tickets cost $5.50. Write and graph an inequality showing the numbers of tickets that would meet the club's goal.

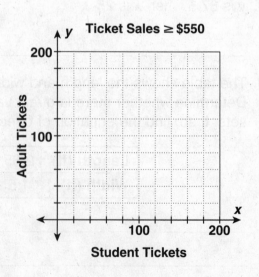

_____

_____

b. If the club sells 95 student tickets and 40 adult tickets, will it meet its goal?

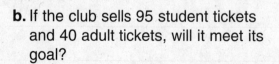

_____

Holt Mathematics

Name _____ Date _____ Class _____

Plot the data and find a line of best fit.

1.

x	20	30	50	60	80	90	110	120
y	13	20	40	54	75	82	100	112

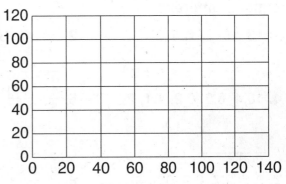

_____

2.

x	1.9	2.9	4.8	2.5	3.9	2.3	6.3	3.4
y	26	34	58	31	52	27	76	48

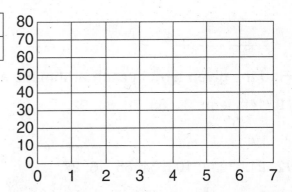

_____

3. Find the line of best fit for the student enrollment data. Use the equation of the line to predict what the enrollment at Columbus Junior High School will be in year 10. Is it reasonable to make this prediction? Explain.

Enrollment	405	485	557	593	638	712
Year	1	2	3	4	5	6

_____

_____

_____

_____

_____

_____

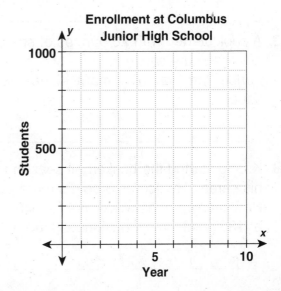

Enrollment at Columbus Junior High School

Holt Mathematics

Name _____ Date _____ Class _____

Determine if each sequence could be arithmetic. If so, give the common difference.

1. 18, 20, 22, 24, 26, ...

2. 48, 42, 36, 30, 24, ...

3. 15, 30, 60, 120, 240, ...

_____   _____   _____

4. 10.4, 8.3, 6.2, 4.1, 2, ...

5. $\frac{1}{3}, \frac{1}{9}, \frac{1}{27}, \frac{1}{81}, \frac{1}{243}$, ...

6. 83, 66, 49, 32, 15, ...

_____   _____   _____

7. 8.1, 2.7, 0.9, 0.3, 0.1, ...

8. $\frac{2}{3}, \frac{4}{3}, 2, \frac{8}{3}, \frac{10}{3}$, ...

9. −58, −35, −12, 11, 34, ...

_____   _____   _____

Find the given term in each arithmetic sequence.

10. 14th term: 60, 68, 76, 84, 92, ...

11. 35th term: 3.5, 3.8, 4.1, 4.4, 4.7, ...

_____   _____

12. 21st term: 103, 84, 65, 46, 27, ...

13. 22nd term: −2, −5, −8, −11, −14, ...

_____   _____

14. 16th term: 73, 44, 15, −14, −43, ...

15. 50th term: −9, 2, 13, 24, 35, ...

_____   _____

16. 19th term: −87, −78, −69, −60, −51, ...

17. 25th term: $3\frac{1}{4}, 3\frac{1}{2}, 3\frac{3}{4}, 4, 4\frac{1}{4}$, ...

_____   _____

18. A cook started with 26 ounces of special sauce. She used 1.4 ounces of the sauce in each of a number of dishes and had 2.2 ounces left over. How many dishes did she make with the sauce?

_____

19. Kuang started the basketball season with 54 points in his career. He scores 3 points more each game he plays. How many games will it take for him to have scored a total of 132 points in his basketball career?

_____

Holt Mathematics

Practice

LESSON
13-2 *Terms of Geometric Sequences*

Determine if each sequence could be geometric. If so, give the common ratio.

1. 4, 16, 64, 256, 1024, ...

2. 3, $\frac{3}{2}$, $\frac{3}{4}$, $\frac{3}{8}$, $\frac{3}{16}$, ...

3. 5, 10, 15, 20, 25, ...

_____   _____   _____

4. 3, 18, 108, 648, 3888, ...

5. 1250, 125, 12.5, 1.25, 0.125, ...

6. 10, 15, 22.5, 33.75, 50.625, ...

_____   _____   _____

7. 36, 12, 4, $\frac{4}{3}$, $\frac{4}{9}$, ...

8. 1440, 720, 240, 60, 12, ...

9. 9, 3, 1, 0.5, 0.25, ...

_____   _____   _____

Find the given term in each geometric sequence.

10. 6th term: 25, 75, 225, 675, ...

11. 10th term: 320, 160, 80, 40, ...

_____   _____

12. 9th term: 4.5, 9, 18, 36, ...

13. 7th term: 0.02, 0.2, 2, 20, ...

_____   _____

14. 12th term: $\frac{1}{1000}$, $\frac{1}{100}$, $\frac{1}{10}$, 1, ...

15. 8th term: $\frac{3}{8}$, $\frac{3}{4}$, $\frac{3}{2}$, 3, ...

_____   _____

16. In an experiment a population of flies triples every week. The experiment starts with 12 flies. How many flies will there be by the end of week 5?

_____

17. A small business earned $21 in its first month. It quadrupled this amount each month for the next several months. How much did the business earn in the 4th month?

_____

Holt Mathematics

LESSON **Practice**
13-3 *Other Sequences*

Use first and second differences to find the next three terms in each sequence.

1. 3, 6, 10, 15, 21, ...

2. 11, 14, 18, 25, 37, ...

_____

3. 10, 16, $22\frac{1}{3}$, 29, 36, ...

4. 14.5, 22.5, 31, 40, 49.5, ...

_____

Give the next three terms in each sequence using the simplest rule you can find.

5. 6, 7, 10, 19, 38, ...

6. 0.5, 2, 4.5, 8, 12.5, ...

_____

7. 36, 55, 80, 111, 148, ...

8. 3, 10, 21, 36, 55, ...

_____

9. 1, 6, 15, 28, 45, ...

10. 0, 11, 30, 57, 92, ...

_____

Find the first five terms of each sequence defined by the given rule.

11. $a_n = \dfrac{n^2 + 2}{n}$

12. $a_n = \dfrac{5n - 2}{n + 1}$

13. $a_n = \dfrac{3n^2}{n + 2}$

_____

14. Suppose *a*, *b*, and *c* are three consecutive numbers in the Fibonacci sequence. Complete the following table and guess the pattern.

a, b, c	ab	bc
1, 1, 2		
2, 3, 5		
5, 8, 13		
13, 21, 34		
34, 55, 89		

_____

Holt Mathematics

Determine whether each function is linear.

1. $f(x) = -3x + 2$

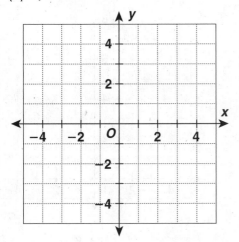

_____

2. $f(x) = x^2 - 1$

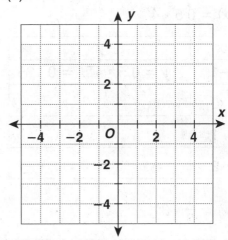

_____

Write a rule for each linear function.

3.

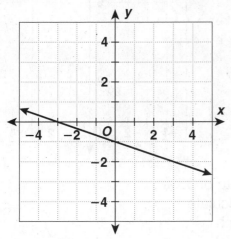

4.

x	y
−3	16
−1	12
3	4
7	−4

_____

_____

5. At the Sweater Store, the price of a sweater is 20% more than the wholesale cost, plus a markup of $8. Find a rule for a linear function that describes the price of sweaters at the Sweater Store. Use it to determine the price of a sweater with a wholesale cost of $24.50.

_____

_____

Holt Mathematics

LESSON **Practice**

13-5 *Exponential Functions*

Create a table for each exponential function, and use it to graph the function.

1. $f(x) = 0.5 \cdot 4^x$

x	y
−1	$y = 0.5 \cdot 4^{-1} = 0.125$
0	
1	
2	

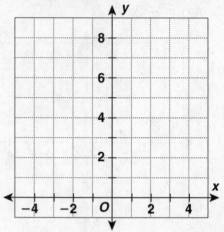

2. $f(x) = \frac{1}{3} \cdot 3^x$

x	y
−1	$y = \frac{1}{3} \cdot 3^{-1} = \frac{1}{9}$
0	
1	
2	

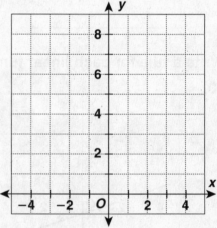

3. A forestry department introduce 500 fish to a lake. The fish are expected to increase at a rate of 35% each year. Write an exponential function to calculate the number of fish in the lake at the end of each year. Predict how many fish will be in the lake at the end of 5 years. _____

4. A stock valued at $756 has been declining steadily at the rate of 4% a year for the last few years. If this decline continues, predict what the value of the stock will be at the end of 3 years. _____

5. Todd's starting salary at his new job is $400 a week. He is promised a 3% increase in salary every year. Predict to the nearest dollar what Todd's expected yearly salary will be after working for 4 years. _____

Holt Mathematics

Name _____ Date _____ Class _____

Create a table for each quadratic function,
and use it to make a graph.

1. $f(x) = x^2 - 5$

x	$f(x) = x^2 - 5$
-3	$f(-3) = (-3)^2 - 5 = 4$
-1	
0	
2	
3	

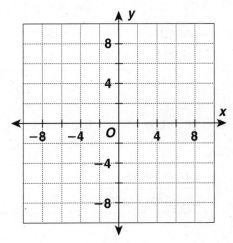

2. $f(x) = x^2 - 2x + 3$

x	$f(x) = x^2 - 2x + 3$
3	
2	
1	
0	
-1	

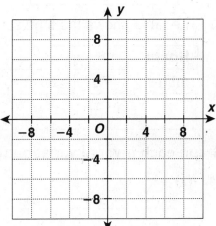

3. Find $f(-3)$, $f(0)$, $f(3)$ for each quadratic function.

	$f(-3)$	$f(0)$	$f(3)$
$f(x) = x^2 - 2x + 1$			
$f(x) = x^2 - 6$			
$f(x) = x^2 - x + 3$			

4. The function $f(t) = -4.9t^2$ gives the distance in meters that an object will fall toward Earth in t seconds. Find the distance an object will fall in 1, 2, 3, 4, and 5 seconds. (Note that the distance traveled by a falling object is shown by a negative number.)

_____

 Holt Mathematics

LESSON Practice
13-7 *Inverse Variation*

Tell whether each relationship is an inverse variation.

1. The table shows the length and width of certain rectangles.

Length	6	8	12	16	24
Width	8	6	4	3	2

_____

2. The table shows the number of days needed to paint a house for the size of the work crew.

Crew Size	2	3	4	5	6
Days of Painting	21	14	10.5	8.5	7

_____

3. The table shows the time spent traveling at different speeds.

Hours	5	6	8	9	12
mi/h	72	60	45	40	30

_____

Graph each inverse variation function.

4. $f(x) = \dfrac{4}{x}$

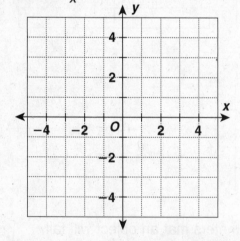

5. $f(x) = \dfrac{5}{x}$

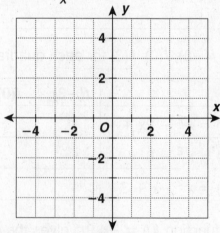

6. Amperes (abbreviated amp) measure the strength of electric current. An ohm is the unit of electrical resistance. In an electric circuit, the current varies inversely as the resistance. If the current is 24 amps when the resistance is 20 ohms, find the inverse variation function and use it to find the resistance in ohms when the current is 40 amps. _____

Holt Mathematics

LESSON Practice
14-1 Polynomials

Determine whether each expression is a monomial.

1. $-135x^5$

2. $2.4x^3y^{19}$

3. $\dfrac{2p^2}{q^3}$

_____

_____

_____

4. $3r^{\frac{1}{2}}$

5. $43a^2b^{6.1}$

6. $\dfrac{7}{9}x^2yz^5$

_____

_____

_____

Classify each expression as a monomial, a binomial, a trinomial, or not a polynomial.

7. $-8.9xy + \dfrac{6}{y^5}$

8. $\dfrac{9}{8}ab^8c^2d$

9. $x^8 + x + 1$

_____

_____

_____

10. $-7pq^{-2}r^4$

11. $5n^{15} - 9n + \dfrac{1}{3}$

12. $r^8 - 5.5r^{75}$

_____

_____

_____

Find the degree of each polynomial.

13. $7 - 14x$

14. $5a + a^2 + \dfrac{6}{7}a^3$

15. $7w - 16u + 3v$

_____

_____

_____

16. $9p - 9q - 9p^3 - 9q^2$

17. $z^9 + 10y^8 - x$

18. $100{,}050 + \dfrac{4}{5}k - k^4$

_____

_____

_____

19. The volume of a box with height x, length $x - 1$, and width $2x + 2$ is given by the trinomial $2x^3 - 2x$. What is the volume of the box if its height is 4 feet?

_____

20. The trinomial $-16t^2 + 32t + 32$ describes the height in feet of a ball thrown upward after t seconds. What is the height of the ball $\dfrac{5}{8}$ seconds after it was thrown?

_____

Holt Mathematics

Name _____ Date _____ Class _____

Identify the like terms in each polynomial.

1. $x^2 - 8x + 3x^2 + 6x - 1$

_____

2. $2c^2 + d^3 + 3d^3 - 2c^2 + 6$

_____

3. $2x^2 - 2xy - 2y^2 + 3xy + 3x^2$

_____

4. $2 - 9x + x^2 - 3 + x$

_____

5. $xy - 5x + y - x + 10y - 3y^2$

_____

6. $6p + 2p^2 + pq + 2q^3 - 2p$

_____

7. $3a + 2b + a^2 - 5b + 7a$

_____

_____

8. $10m - 3m^2 + 9m^2 - 3m - m^3$

_____

_____

Simplify.

9. $2h - 9hk + 6h - 6k$

_____

10. $9(x^2 + 2xy - y^2) - 2(x^2 + xy)$

_____

11. $7qr - q^2r^3 + 2q^2r^3 - 6qr$

_____

12. $8v^4 + 3v^2 + 2v^2 - 16$

_____

13. $3(x + 2y) + 2(2x - 3y)$

_____

14. $7(1 - x) + 3x^2y + 7x - 7$

_____

15. $6(9y + 1) + 8(2 - 3y)$

_____

16. $a^2b - a^2 + ab^2 - 3a^2b + ab$

_____

17. A student in Tracey's class created the following expression:
$y^3 - 3y + 4(y^2 - y^3)$. Use the Distributive Property to write
an equivalent expression.

_____

Holt Mathematics

Practice

Adding Polynomials

Add.

1. $(a^2 + a + 3) + (15a^2 + 2a + 9)$

2. $(5x + 2x^2) + (3x - 2x^2)$

_____

_____

3. $(mn - 10 + mn^2) + (5 + 3mn - 4mn^2)$ **4.** $(7y^2z + 9 + yz^2) + (y^2z - 2yz^2)$

_____

_____

5. $(s^3 + 3s - 3) + (2s^3 + 9s - 2) + (s - s^3)$

_____

6. $(6wv - 4w^2v + 7wv^2) + (5w^2v - 7wv^2) + (wv^2 - 5wv + 6w^2v)$

_____

7. $(6b^2c^2 - 4b^2c + 3bc) + (9b^2c^2 - 4bc + 12) + (2b^2c - 3bc - 8)$

_____

8. $(7e^2 + 3e + 2) + (9 - 6e + 4e^2) + (9e + 2 - 6e^2) + (4e^2 - 7e + 8)$

_____

9. $(f^4g - fg^3 + 2fg - 4) + (3fg^3 + 3) + (4f^4g - 5fg) + (3 - 12fg^3 + f^4g)$

_____

10. Six blocks of height $4h + 4$ each and 3 blocks of height $8 - 2h$
each are stacked on top of each other to form one big tower.
Find an expression for the overall height of the tower.

_____

105 **Holt Mathematics**

LESSON 14-4 Practice

Subtracting Polynomials

Find the opposite of each polynomial.

1. $18xy^3$ 　　　　　　　　**2.** $-9a + 4$ 　　　　　　　**3.** $6d^2 - 2d - 8$

_____　　　_____　　　_____

Subtract.

4. $(4n^3 - 4n + 4n^2) - (6n + 3n^2 - 8)$ 　　**5.** $(-2h^4 + 3h - 4) - (2h - 3h^4 + 2)$

_____　　　　　　　　_____

6. $(6m + 2m^2 - 7) - (-6m^2 - m - 7)$ 　　**7.** $(17x^2 - x + 3) - (14x^2 + 3x + 5)$

_____　　　　　　　　_____

8. $w + 7 - (3w^4 + 5w^3 - 7w^2 + 2w - 10)$

_____

9. $(9r^3s - 3rs + 4rs^3 + 5r^2s^2) - (2rs^2 - 2r^2s^2 + 6rs + 7r^3s - 9)$

_____

10. $(3qr^2 - 2 + 14q^2r^2 - 9qr) - (-10qr + 11 - 5qr^2 + 6q^2r^2)$

_____

11. The volume of a rectangular prism, in cubic meters, is given by
the expression $x^3 + 7x^2 + 14x + 8$. The volume of a smaller
rectangular prism is given by the expression $x^3 + 5x^2 + 6x$.
How much greater is the volume of the larger rectangular prism?

_____

12. Sarah has a table with an area, in square inches, given by the
expression of $y^2 + 30y + 200$. She has a tablecloth with an area,
in square inches, given by the expression of $y^2 + 18y + 80$.
She wants the tablecloth to cover the top of the table. What
expression represents the number of square inches of additional
fabric she needs to cover the top of the table?

_____

　　　　　　106　　　　　　**Holt Mathematics**

Name _____ Date _____ Class _____

Multiply.

1. $(x^2)(-3x^2y^3)$

     _____

2. $(-9pr^4)(p^2r^2)$

     _____

3. $(2st^9)(-st^2)$

     _____

4. $(3efg^2)(-3e^2f^2g)$

     _____

5. $2q(4q^2 - 2)$

     _____

6. $-x(x^2 + 2)$

     _____

7. $5m(-3m^2 + 2m)$

     _____

8. $6x(-x^5 + 2x^3 + x)$

     _____

9. $-4st(st - 12t - 2s)$

     _____

10. $-9ab(a^2 + 2ab - b^2)$

     _____

11. $-7v^2w^2(vw^2 + 2vw + 1)$

     _____

12. $8p^4(p^2 - 8p + 17)$

     _____

13. $4x(-x^2 - 2xy + 3)$

     _____

14. $7x^2(3x^2y + 7x^2 - 2x)$

     _____

15. $-4t^3r^2(3t^2r - t^5r - 6t^2r^2)$

     _____

16. $h^2k(2hk^2 - hk + 7k)$

     _____

17. A triangle has a base of $4x^2$ and a height of $6x + 3$. Write and simplify an expression for the area of the triangle.

_____

Holt Pre-Algebra

LESSON **Practice**
14-6 *Multiplying Binomials*

Multiply.

1. $(z + 1)(z + 2)$

2. $(1 - y)(2 - y)$

3. $(2x + 1)(2x + 4)$

_____

_____

_____

4. $(w + 1)(w - 3)$

5. $(3v + 1)(v - 1)$

6. $(t + 2)(2t - 2)$

_____

_____

_____

7. $(-3g + 4)(2g - 1)$

8. $(3c + d)(c - 2d)$

9. $(2a + b)(a + 2b)$

_____

_____

_____

10. A box is formed from a 1 in. by 18 in. piece of cardboard by cutting a square with side length m inches out of each corner and folding up the sides. Write and simplify an expression for the area of the base of the box.

_____

11. A table is placed in a 14 ft × 18 ft room so that there is an equal amount of space of width s feet all the way around the table. Write and simplify an expression for the area of the table.

_____

12. A circular swimming pool with a radius of 14 ft is surrounded by a deck with width y feet. Write and simplify an expression for the total area of the pool and the deck. Use $\frac{22}{7}$ for pi.

_____

Multiply.

13. $(r - 2)^2$

14. $(2 + q)^2$

15. $(p + 4)(p - 4)$

_____

_____

_____

16. $(3n - 3)(3n + 3)$

17. $(a + b)(a - b)$

18. $(4e - f)^2$

_____

_____

_____

19. $(2y + z)^2$

20. $(9p - 2)(-2 + 9p)$

21. $(m - 1)^2$

_____

_____

_____

Holt Mathematics